Clay Preparation and Shaping

F. J. GOODSON

The following is a list of the titles comprised in this series of books.

The Geology and Mineralogy of Brick Clays—P. S. Keeling, B.SC., A.R.S.M., F.G.S.

Clay Winning and Haulage—C. R. Atkinson, B.SC., F.G.S., A.I. Ceram.

Clay Preparation and Shaping—F. J. Goodson, B.SC., M.I. MECH. E., F.I. Ceram.

The Drying of Bricks—R. W. Ford, B.SC.

Fuels, Combustion and Heat Transfer—A. E. Aldersley, M.INST.F., A.I. Ceram.

The Firing of Bricks—E. Rowden, B.SC., A.R.C.S., D.I.C., F.R.I.C., F.I. Ceram.

The Layout of Brickworks—H. W. H. West, B.SC., F.G.S., F.I. Ceram.

© 1962   Brick Development Association Limited.

Printed in England by Thos. Forman & Sons Ltd. Nottingham.

Preface

This book, commissioned by the Brick Development Association Limited, is one of a series, the titles of which are shown on the opposite page. The series is designed to cover the main aspects of building-brick production, from the winning of the clay to the firing of the brick in the kiln.

Primarily intended for those whose daily work lies in the brickmaking industry, it is hoped that the series will also be of assistance to students and of interest to those whose work is only indirectly concerned with clay and bricks.

The Association wishes to place on record its thanks to all those who, by their help and co-operation, assisted in the production of this book. It is especially indebted to Dr. A. T. Green, C.B.E., D.SC., F.R.I.C., Hon. F.I. Ceram., formerly Director of the British Ceramic Research Association, and to Messrs. T. G. W. Boxall, O.B.E., B.SC., A.C.G.I., A.M.I.C.E., F.I. Ceram. and M. S. Whitehouse, C.B.E., B.A., F.I. Ceram., who have assisted in the editing of the series as a whole.

Author's Note

The material contained in this book is drawn largely from the knowledge and experience that has been gained through my close association with the industry over a number of years.

By the extensive use of illustrations I have attempted to compensate for the deliberately brief descriptions of the various machines that are dealt with in the text, and my thanks are due to all those machinery manufacturers, whose names are listed at the back of the book, for their permission to use the illustrations that appear in the text. It should be made quite clear that most of the machines illustrated are made by all the brickmaking machinery manufacturers, and the fact that each machine illustrated is attributed to only one manufacturer merely indicates that that particular illustration was, in my view, the one most effective for the purposes of this book.

My thanks are also due to Mr. F. H. Clews for allowing me to use certain illustrations which appear in his own book *Heavy Clay Technology*, and to the various other members of the Staff of the British Ceramic Research Association for their assistance in reading and checking proofs, obtaining blocks and preparing suitable drawings.

I trust that our combined efforts have resulted in a book which the reader will find to be not only of interest, but also of real practical value.

F. J. Goodson, B.SC., M.I.MECH.E., F.I. Ceram.
British Ceramic Research Association
Queens Road
Penkhull
Stoke-on-Trent

Contents

Introduction

The shaping of articles from clay is one of the oldest of human occupations. Just when the art was first practised is not known, but from excavations made in various parts of the world it would appear that it was practised, many thousands of years ago, in countries separated by oceans with no apparent means of communication, so there is no doubt that it was discovered independently by many different nations and races.

When the first clayware article was hardened by firing is not known but the use of wood fires for baking clayware was a great advance in the art since its durability and usefulness was thereby increased.

The history of ceramics is older than the recorded history of mankind and much has been learned of the stage of culture reached in bygone civilizations by a study of the texture, shape, decoration and method of firing the fragments of pottery, tiles and bricks which have been excavated by archaeologists.

Methods of Shaping: The earliest bricks were made by hand-shaping and, later, wooden moulds were made in order to make all bricks of the same size. The moulds were wetted to prevent the clay from sticking to the moulds which were filled by hand, a method still used. The best quality bricks, even today, are the hand-made bricks because if properly made they are free from laminations or pressure cracks which are sometimes evident in bricks made mechanically. In spite of this the majority of bricks today are made mechanically. So, after thousands of years as a craft industry we have now reached the stage where the shaping of clayware is an automatic operation, carried out by mechanical robots which have no pride of craftsmanship, and cannot differentiate between different bodies, so that the prepared body must always be as near perfect and uniform as possible.

Even for hand-making the clay is prepared by machinery, but neither a hand-maker nor a machine can make good bricks from badly prepared clay.

An intelligent hand-maker however has a great advantage over any machine. He can tell by the feel of the clay whether it is in a suitable condition for shaping. If not, he himself can do some more work on it. He can add a little more water if necessary, he can knead and wedge up the clay to improve it, and he can usually express his mind and give vent to his feelings in no uncertain way so that the man responsible for preparing the clay is in no doubt what is wrong with it and can immediately take steps to put it right. There is no machine in existence that can do this, or that can alter the amount or the nature of the work it does on a clay to suit variations.

Hand-makers work with fine-grained plastic clays. Their main problem is to get the clay into such a consistency that it will flow into the corners of the mould to form a well-shaped brick. Laminations are often present but they are so irregular as not to damage the brick.

Laminations which give rise to flaking, cracking or fractures appear mainly in machine-made bricks and for this reason the machine is usually blamed. This is one of the main faults which the engineer and the brick-maker have to try to prevent. It is not a problem that the engineer can solve without the active co-operation and support of the brickmaker.

At the majority of brickworks there is seldom a long run during which all bricks are faulty. If all bricks are faulty, even for a short time, something has obviously gone wrong and a determined effort is made to find the cause and it is put right at the earliest possible moment. Faults in bricks are usually of a random nature, they occur occasionally, usually in odd bricks and the total rarely exceeds a few per cent of the total made. To cure these faults it is necessary to look for random variations in the prepared body and to so control the clay, and the preparation of it, as to obtain as uniformly consistent a body as possible.

When we start looking for variations we soon find that the raw materials used for brickmaking are themselves variable. This is not surprising when one considers the mechanism of clay formation and deposition, which occurred millions of years ago. Along with the clay was deposited non-clay minerals such as sand, chalk, limestone, pyrites and other stones of an assorted nature, shells and organic matter in varying degree. These impurities may occur in layers, in discreet pockets, or randomly dispersed, and they may be present in large pieces, small nodules or fine particles. Not only are all clay-pits different but, in some, samples taken from borings as close as two feet apart will show marked variations in analysis. From such a heterogeneous material the brickmaker has to make bricks and wonders why he gets random faulty ones. The first step in eliminating faulty bricks is therefore to try to get a uniformly consistent raw material and this can only be done by bulk blending the clay from the whole face in as large quantities as possible.

Having taken precautions to get a uniform raw material the next step is grinding.

Generally the clay minerals are of fine structure and will break down to very fine particles in water, but the time required to break down the clays by this means varies considerably according to the nature of the clay mineral, and to the pressure, temperature and amount of weathering to which it has been subjected whilst still a part of the earth's crust. By breaking down the clay into small agglomerations of particles it becomes much easier for the water to penetrate between the individual clay particles, which is so necessary to obtain uniform water distribution and to develop optimum plasticity. This is achieved by grinding. It is not generally necessary to weather the clay.

Some of the non-clay minerals present in the deposit are undesirable such as those which cause scumming or efflorescence, but this trouble can usually be overcome by the addition of salts, whilst those which cause undesirable spots or blemishes such as iron spots or lime-bursting can frequently be overcome by finer grinding. Most of the non-clay minerals are however desirable. If a brick was made from a pure clay mineral the drying shrinkage would be excessive, the water would have great difficulty in getting out and in doing so would fill the brick with cracks so that it would probably not hold together. In order to open up the body to allow the escape of water during drying and firing without cracking the brick, to reduce shrinkage and to develop the strength of the brick some inert, coarse material is needed. This is provided by the non-clay minerals in the deposit. Apart from this, some of the non-clay minerals impart a characteristic colour to the brick, which is so desirable, but to develop a uniform colour these should be ground to such a size that they can be uniformly distributed throughout the brick. Grinding and thorough mixing is therefore essential.

2

Another thing which affects the physical properties of the bricks is the bulk density. If all bricks are made at the same pressure with the same water content the thing which affects the bulk density, and crushing strength, is the grading analysis. Every effort should therefore be made to control the grading analysis. This usually amounts to control of the rate of feed to the grinder and more rigorous maintenance of the grinding plant. However, even if the grading analysis from the screens is reasonably consistent there is always the risk of destroying this by segregation. Every effort should therefore be made to prevent segregation between the screens and the tempering operation.

By tempering is meant the addition of the correct amount of water and its thorough incorporation into the clay body. For any given clay the amount of water necessary is critical for the particular making process and generally speaking the lower the water content the higher the forming pressure necessary to shape the brick. Different clays, however, require different water contents to develop the same consistency of clay body, which means that different clays need different amounts of water for the same making processes.

Whatever the amount of water necessary for a particular method of shaping, it is essential that it should be thoroughly and intimately mixed throughout the whole of the body; it is no use having some of the clay too soft and some too dry because this would inevitably lead to trouble.

Since there are so many different clays and shales, which vary widely in their properties, and since each contains different, or different amounts of, impurities it is not surprising that the preparation most suited for one is not necessarily the most suitable for another. For the same reason a large number of different types of clay-preparation machines are available.

For this reason a discussion on the shaping of clays can only be complete if it also includes clay preparation.

1 : Clay Preparation

Whatever the method of shaping adopted, the shaping machine does not prepare the body from which the bricks are made. It cannot make better bricks than the clay body fed to it will allow and if there should be any variation in the clay body there is bound to be a variation in the physical properties of the bricks made.

The object of clay preparation is to obtain, at all times, a clay body so blended as to have a uniform clay content, ground to a constant grading analysis, thoroughly mixed and tempered with the correct amount of water for the particular method of shaping. The higher the quality of bricks required, the greater must be the control over the various stages of preparation and it is only by continuity of control that a high standard of quality can be maintained.

Bulk Storage and Blending: Modern methods of line production necessitate a continuous flow of material from the point of winning to the finished product, but it is always good practice to provide bulk storage at strategic points in the line to allow production to carry on if, for any reason, some part of the plant fails to function.

3

For example, during inclement weather it may not be possible to win clay for several days, or maybe weeks, at a time and to prevent stoppage of production a bulk store of raw clay should be provided at some convenient position between winning and grinding. Generally more room will be available at the clay-pit than at the works, so the logical choice would be to locate the bulk clay store at the pit. This clay store should however not be looked upon as a reserve supply to be used only in case of emergency. If a raw clay store is to be made then it should be made properly so that it can perform a useful function. The particular useful function to be achieved depends upon the nature of the clay available. It may be weathering or bulk blending but most clay-pits would definitely benefit by bulk blending.

Weathering: The weathering of clays is often resorted to in order to improve their working properties. By weathering is meant exposing the clay, as won, to the action of the weather. This exposure to the weather affects the clay both physically and chemically.

The physical changes are mainly disintegration of the clay due to expansion and contraction caused by freezing and thawing, by wetting by rain and the drying action of the wind, by variation in temperature by day and by night. Rain tends to wash out some of the soluble salts and so reduces the tendency to scum.

The chemical changes are due to hydration and hydrolysis from saturation by rain, oxidation due to the action of the air and carbonization due to the action of carbon dioxide in solution in the water.

There is also probably some biological change due to the action of bacteria which is claimed to increase the plasticity of the clay.

Of these the most important changes are the physical changes and these can usually be achieved much better, quicker and more cheaply by mechanical means and this is why it is claimed that weathering is unnecessary for the majority of clays. The chemical and biological changes can not be achieved by machine and it is only when these are important that weathering should be practised.

In preparing a weathering heap it should be remembered that the action of the weather rarely penetrates more than a few inches so that the clay should be spread for weathering in a thin layer over a large area.

Bulk Blending: It cannot be denied that the majority of the troubles encountered in brickmaking are due to variations in the clay body supplied to the making machines. These variations are due to variations in composition of the clay as won at the clay face, which are of a random nature and, without special sampling techniques, are often difficult to detect. To reduce the effect of these variations the clay from the whole of the working face in the clay-pit should be blended together, in as large a volume as possible, so that the variations in the clay fed to the preparation plant are reduced considerably. To do this satisfactorily two blending heaps are necessary, one being made whilst from the other the clay is being rewon and fed to the preparation plant. This method of bulk blending was pioneered by American manufacturers in order to obtain a consistent body. At first, only the larger manufacturers adopted it but the results were so successful that many other manufacturers have followed suit. Many of the American blending heaps are very large and hold thousands of tons of clay.

The blending heaps must be properly constructed if they are to blend the clay satisfactorily. When the clay is won vertically such as by blasting, by bucket excavator or by dragline, the face is won in sections, each section comprising a rough mixture of all the seams at that part of the face. Usually with such methods of winning, the clay contains many large pieces that are unsuitable for the blending heap so the clay, as won, should be fed to a primary crusher before laying on the blending heap. After primary crushing, the whole of the clay from that section is spread over the whole area of the blending heap, being spread and levelled by means of a mechanical rake, scraper, or bulldozer. The next section is treated in the same way and laid and spread on top of the first layer. This is continued until clay from the whole of the face has been laid section by section one on top of the other and the process is again repeated building up the blending heap to a convenient height (say about ten feet) so that the clay can be rewon vertically by a mechanical shovel, or bucket excavator, for feeding to the preparation plant. By this means the preparation plant is fed with a mixture comprising small amounts from each part of the face.

By winning the clay from the pit-face vertically, a rough mixture of all the seams in the pit is obtained but the composition of the mix will vary at different places along the face. By constructing the blending heap horizontally and winning from it vertically the composition of the mix fed to the preparation plant is more nearly uniform and troubles due to random variations in the clay composition are consequently considerably reduced.

If the clay is easily friable so that it can be won by a scraper then the face can be won in benches, say 20 to 30 feet wide, each bench comprising one seam of clay. In this case there will be no large pieces and so there is no need for a primary crusher. The advantage of the scraper is that it can win and transport the clay to the blending heap where it can lay it down and level it off. Each seam is laid and levelled flat one above the other until the blending heap has attained the desired height.

An alternative method of winning by scraper is to win on an incline from bottom to top of the face so that each load consists of a proportion of all the seams which make up the face. Each load is laid and levelled on the blending heap as before and is rewon vertically.

Such blending heaps are usually covered with a light roof to protect them from rain and, apart from the advantages of blending, these large heaps provide a bulk store of clay which can be drawn upon when normal winning is impossible.

When the main bulk clay store, or blending heap, is situated at the clay-pit it is often advisable to have a second, smaller, clay store at the works, adjacent to the mill to serve as insurance against breakdown of the transport or haulage system from the pit to the works. It should be sufficient to keep the works running at full output for at least a whole day.

Ground Clay Store: If the clay is ground in a dry pan and screened, it is usual to maintain a store of screened clay. Generally this is stored on the floor of a dust loft from which the ground clay is fed through holes in the floor to chutes, conveyors or pipes, to the subsequent processing machines.

Dust lofts are notoriously dusty places and arching or bridging of the clay over the holes frequently occurs, necessitating manual operation to keep the clay flowing. If for any reason grinding has to stop for some time and clay is still being used from the dust floor serious troubles may be encountered, because manual labour will be necessary to feed the clay to the discharge hole. The accumulation of dust on the floor is in the form of a large cone and in forming this cone segregation has inevitably occurred, the larger particles rolling down the incline to the base. When hand-feeding from the dust floor there will be a variation in grading analysis; sometimes the feed will be mainly fines and sometimes mainly coarse. This is bound to affect the properties of the bricks made. There will be variation in texture, variation in colour, and variation in crushing strength and absorption.

For these reasons it is always better to store the ground clay in hoppers specially designed to prevent both segregation and arching. Such hoppers minimize the amount of dust in the general atmosphere of the works, an important feature of 'good housekeeping'.

Segregation: When a falling stream of particles is arrested they collect in the form of a cone. The fine particles remain where they land, being unable to roll over coarser particles, but the larger particles, possessing greater momentum, roll freely over the conical bed of small particles and travel towards the periphery of the base. If a hopper is filled by means of a central stream of material, as by a conveyor or elevator, there will be a preponderance of fines at the centre and a preponderance of coarse material at the outside.

If the hopper is discharged through a central orifice in the bottom of the discharge cone there will be, at first, an excess of fines as the centre comes down, then when an inverted cone has been formed at the free surface the product will be fairly uniform, and towards the end of discharge, when the hopper is almost empty, there will be an excess of coarse material.

Overcoming Segregation: If the hopper has a central feed a simple improvement is to direct the stream of material onto the apex of a cone which deflects the material to be deposited in a ring half-way between the hopper wall and the central axis (Fig. 1). This does not prevent segregation but reduces its effect.

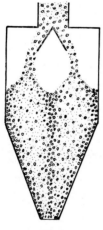

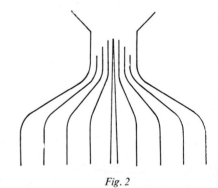

Fig. 2

Fig. 1

Methods of reducing segregation

A better way of overcoming segregation is to allow the feed to fall on to a distributor consisting of a number of concentric cones (Fig. 2). This distributes the material more uniformly across the cross-section of the hopper.

Another method of overcoming segregation is to use a rotating silo. This consists of a steel cylinder, open at top and bottom, supported on a central vertical shaft so that its open bottom is a few inches above a solid disc

6

base which is also mounted on the shaft. The shaft is supported in a substantial footstep bearing at the bottom and a radial bearing at the top. The disc base is fitted with a central cone on its upper face to feed the ground clay towards the periphery during discharge. The central shaft, complete with cylinder and disc baseplate, is slowly rotated at a speed of about 4 r.p.m. and the ground clay is fed in at the top of the cylinder, by a belt conveyor from the screen, at a point about midway between the cylinder wall and the central shaft. Discharge is from the bottom by means of an adjustable scraper which ploughs the ground clay from the disc base onto a conveyor which carries it to the next process. A rotating silo 11 feet diameter by 15 feet deep holds about 50 tons of ground clay and requires a 5-h.p. motor to drive it.

Ageing or Conditioning Plastic Clay: The bulk storage of ground and tempered wet or plastic clay is not so general in this country as it is on the continent of Europe. There ageing or conditioning pits, capable of storing three months' or more supply of ground and tempered plastic clay are frequently encountered.

These ageing or conditioning pits are concrete lined and are roofed over to protect the clay from the elements. They are filled continuously, usually by an overhead belt conveyor which feeds onto a reversible, travelling, transverse belt conveyor and at the same time the conditioned clay is being rewon continuously by means of a multi-bucket excavator traversing the face of the clay over the width of the pit. The excavator discharges to a transverse belt conveyor, which travels with the excavator, and discharges to a main belt which conveys the clay to the final preparation machines. The mean rate of winning is the same as the mean rate of filling so that the pit is always full, and the new face being laid down is only a short distance behind the face being won. Water, as required, is sprayed onto the new face in the form of a fine mist from spray nozzles and the whole of the pit is under cover to protect it from rain, wind and direct sunshine. By this means the water content is controlled.

When the multi-bucket excavator reaches the end of the pit, it is raised and traverses back the full length of the pit to the other end where it is lowered and winning is recommenced. Meanwhile clay continues to be fed into the pit until the end is reached when the gantry carrying the transverse belt conveyor, the plough on the main longitudinal conveyor, and the spray nozzles travel back to the beginning and loading of the pit recommences.

A typical ageing or conditioning pit is shown by Figs. 3 and 4. Fig. 3 is a view along the length of the pit showing the newly-laid face and the fine spray of water from the nozzles falling on the new face. The multi-bucket excavator is seen in the foreground winning the conditioned clay and Fig. 4 is taken from the opposite end showing the multi-bucket excavator with its transverse conveyor. Overhead can be seen the transverse feed conveyor over the top of which is the main feed conveyor which runs the full length of the pit. The transverse conveyor has a length equal to half the width of the pit and is mounted on a carriage which traverses half the width of the pit the whole being supported on a gantry which travels intermittently along the length of the pit. With the carriage in one extreme position, and the top portion of the belt moving towards the centre of the pit, the clay will be discharged onto the face at the centre. The carriage travels slowly across, feeding the clay onto the face from the centre to the side wall. When

Figs. 3 and 4   Conditioning Pits

the side wall is reached the direction of movement of the belt and the carriage are automatically reversed so that the other half of the face is loaded from the centre to the side wall. The gantry then moves forward a few inches and the process of filling the pit continues automatically. Meanwhile the multi-bucket excavator, also mounted on a gantry, traverses the full width of the pit and then inches forward a little for the return journey. It discharges to a transverse belt conveyor, mounted on the gantry, and this in turn discharges to the main discharge conveyor.

It is usually claimed that in these conditioning pits the water distribution becomes more uniform, but tests indicate that there is little or no migration of water from a region of high water content to one of low water content even after long periods. There is therefore no redistribution of the water but the advantage of ageing is that it allows ample time for the water to soak between the individual clay particles, so breaking down the clay and developing optimum plasticity. Pits also assist bulk blending so tending to make the clay body more uniform. They occupy a considerable floor area, a pit 240 feet long by 60 feet wide by 15 feet deep will hold about 9,000 tons of clay which is sufficient for three months' making at the rate of 4,000 bricks per hour. They are expensive in initial cost but are economical to run and are usually attended by one man only, who also attends to the maintenance of the equipment.

Conditioning Tower or Maukturm: Another continental development is the use of conditioning towers, Maukturms, in place of the conditioning pits. These are tall cylindrical or conical towers which hold sufficient ground wet or plastic clay to supply the making machines with a minimum of at least one day's production requirements. The argument in favour of these is that conditioning is more effective and quicker if it takes place under pressure and is most beneficial during the first 12 to 24 hours. Whilst this argument might be true for a number of clays it must be pointed out that all clays do not need the same amount of ageing and indeed many can be shaped without any at all, whilst some of the more obstinate require much more than 24 hours. It therefore pays to study the clays available and to experiment with them to see if any advantage is to be gained by ageing and if so what is the optimum time required.

A typical Maukturm is illustrated by Fig. 5. It consists of a slowly rotating base, driven through gearing from an electric motor, and a stationary conical shell, about 12 feet diameter at the base by 25 feet high, having a capacity of about 100 tons of clay. Inside is a combined mixing and conveying screw; the clay is fed in at the top and the conditioned clay is discharged at the bottom.

Fig. 5 Maukturm

2 : Primary Crushing and Clay Cleaning

Grinding plays an essential part in the preparation of clay bodies. Its object is to break down the clay minerals to a size most suitable for the uniform adsorption of water and to grind the non-clay minerals to such a fineness that they can be thoroughly blended with the clay to develop optimum strength, a consistent colour and uniform body texture.

The method of grinding varies somewhat with the nature of the clay as won and the method of manufacture. In this country the clay is usually won dry and for dry grinding a dry pan is generally used. It should however be remembered that a dry pan is essentially a secondary grinder. It is not intended to break down large lumps of hard material, but the dry pan is so accommodating that it is all too often that large pieces of hard clay are fed to the dry pan. If this is done the pan needs to run at a lower speed, thus reducing its output below the maximum possible, increasing wear and consequently costs of maintenance. When large pieces of hard material are encountered in the feed they should first be crushed in a primary crusher, because coarse crushing is cheaper when done in a primary crusher which is designed specially for this purpose. Also the smaller the size of the feed to the dry pan the greater its output and the lower its power consumption and maintenance costs. The size of the feed to a pan mill should not generally exceed about two to three inches.

If the raw clay contains large pieces it should be fed on to a grizzly screen to remove all pieces above this size. The fines would fall through the grizzly screen on to a belt conveyor which also passes under the primary crusher to the pan or preferably to a storage hopper with mechanical discharge which serves as a bulk store and also evens out the feed to the pan. The coarse material, which does not pass through the grizzly screen, discharges directly to the primary crusher which crushes the lumps to about two inches in size and the crushed clay falls onto the conveyor below onto the fines which have gone through the grizzly screen.

When two or more clays or shales are to be mixed they should preferably be crushed separately in a primary crusher and stored in separate storage bins from which they can be accurately proportioned into the secondary grinder which is usually a dry pan.

Primary Crushers: Five types of primary crusher are used in the heavy clay industries, some being in quite common use and some of which are used by a very few concerns. The types are:

1. Jaw Crushers.
2. Gyratory Crushers.
3. Double-roll Crushers.
4. Single-roll Crushers.
5. Swing-hammer Mills.

Of these the jaw crusher, double-roll crusher and single-roll crusher are most generally used.

The type of clay to be crushed generally determines the type of primary crusher to be used. Thus if clays are friable and have no tendency to pack between the crushing jaws, jaw crushers or gyratory crushers may be used. If the clay tends to pack in the jaws there is a risk of bursting such machines. For those clays which can be ground in these types of crusher the jaw crusher can be built with greater strength than the gyratory crusher and for the same size of crushed product the feed opening of the jaw crusher is larger than that of the gyratory crusher, so that it is capable of crushing larger feed sizes. On the other hand if the feed is not too large in size then for the same size reduction the gyratory crusher, on account of its larger crushing area, will crush at a faster rate than the jaw crusher.

For materials which tend to pack between the crusher jaws the double-roll, single-roll or swing-hammer type of crusher should be used.

Jaw Crushers: There are three main types of jaw crusher, the principal difference in design being in the motion of the jaws. Detail differences in design in any one type are made by different manufacturers but the principle of operation of the different types is shown by Fig. 6. Blake type crushers provide maximum movement on the smallest pieces, Dodge crushers greatest movement on the largest pieces and the single-toggle machines are a modification of the two basic types.

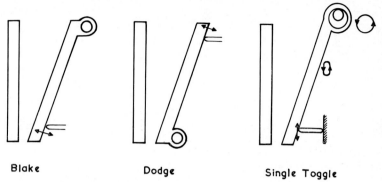

Blake   Dodge   Single Toggle

Fig. 6   Principles of operation—Jaw Crushers

The features on which a proper choice of crusher depends can be briefly enumerated as follows. Blake type crushers have large capacity per unit length of feed opening, but as the maximum movement of the jaw is at the smallest opening, the crusher will not make a uniformly sized product. Providing all fines of product size and less are removed ahead of the crusher a Blake crusher will crush to approximately 50 per cent minus the closed side setting and approximately 75 per cent minus the open side setting of the swing jaw. The minimum closed side setting on the smallest machines is about ⅜ inch.

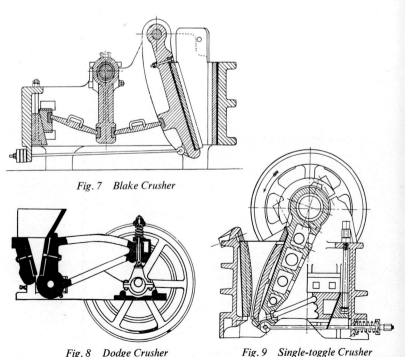

Fig. 7   Blake Crusher

Fig. 8   Dodge Crusher   Fig. 9   Single-toggle Crusher

Dodge type jaw crushers have relatively low capacities, but the products are of uniform size, averaging about 80 per cent minus the discharge setting. The minimum practical discharge setting is about ½ inch.

Single-toggle crushers, having the eccentric mounted in the top of the swing jaw, will crush rock to about 85 per cent minus the open side setting and about 50 per cent minus the closed side setting. They therefore give a more uniform product than the Blake crusher and the capacity is high. Single-toggle jaw crushers have not proved practical in large sizes because the weight of the heavy swing jaw imposes severe strains on the eccentric bearings, but they are suitable for throughputs of up to about 25 tons per hour.

Cross sections of the three types are illustrated by Figs. 7, 8, and 9.

Gyratory Crushers: For capacities which are higher than can be obtained from a Blake crusher, or when it is desired to produce a granular product from a slabby feed, primary gyratory crushers should be used. A typical gyratory crusher is shown in cross section by Fig. 10.

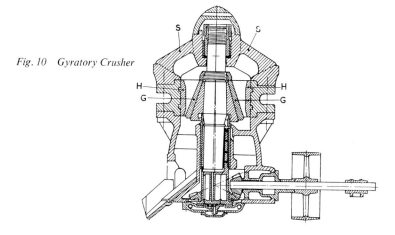

Fig. 10   Gyratory Crusher

The principle of crushing is similar to that of the Blake jaw crushers, the crushing jaws being circular instead of flat. Because of this the crushing area of a gyratory crusher is greater than that of a jaw crusher for the same feed and product size and consequently greater outputs are obtained. The machine consists of a central vertical shaft which gyrates but does not revolve, being supported in a rotating eccentric bearing at the bottom whilst the top of the shaft is supported in a self-aligning bearing. The shaft therefore moves with a gyratory motion. On the shaft is mounted a renewable conical crushing head or mantle 'G' and surrounding it is the housing which contains renewable crushing plates or concaves 'H'. The upper self-aligning bearing is mounted in a bridge 'S' which is rigidly attached to the housing and bridges across the opening in the top. Feeding, therefore, can be from both sides of this bridge. With the gyratory motion of the shaft, the crushing cone is constantly approaching and receding from the shell-liners so that the closed setting between the crushing head and the concaves moves round the periphery of the crushing jaws thus ensuring uniform wear. Crushing takes place all round the cones as they approach each other and each lump, once cracked, settles lower down for another blow at the next gyration, or is discharged if already fine enough.

Choice of Crushing Surfaces: The crushing jaw plates of jaw crushers and the mantles and concaves of gyratory crushers may be straight or curved, the curved plates being termed non-choking plates. The difference in operation between the two types is shown by Fig. 11 which shows that, for the same size of feed and product and the same jaw movement, the material is ground in fewer strokes with the non-choking plate. This is due to the shape of the plate which after each stroke allows the material to fall farther than with the straight plate. This ensures that the material flows through the jaws at a faster rate so reducing the tendency to choke and giving a greater throughput. The shape of the crushing surface also serves to give a nearly parallel zone towards the discharge end so that the product is more nearly uniform in size than that obtained with straight surfaces.

For many crushers, non-choking jaw plates are made reversible so that when the discharge section begins to wear, owing to the greater crushing action at that point, the entire crushing plate can be reversed.

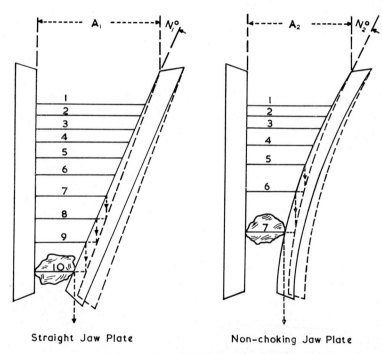

Straight Jaw Plate   Non-choking Jaw Plate

Fig. 11   Straight and non-choking grinding plates

Double-roll Crushers: These are probably the most popular type of primary crusher in use in the heavy clay industry. Double-roll crushers may be obtained with smooth rolls, rolls with breaker bars, projections, corrugations or teeth.

Smooth rolls are not usually used for primary crushing but are very largely used for secondary grinding. The others have projections or teeth to grip the material to be crushed so that larger pieces can be crushed than would be possible with smooth rolls. Such rolls are frequently termed Kibbling rolls although strictly speaking Kibbling rolls have toothed rollers

14

built up of two opposing and interspaced sets of toothed star-wheels or 'kibblers' which break up the materials to be crushed similar to those illustrated by Fig. 12, those having hooked teeth being used for soft and somewhat plastic clays. Rolls with projections, Fig. 13, are termed cubing rolls and are useful for breaking down hard slabby material to give a more cube-like product for feeding to the secondary grinder. Fig. 14 illustrates the rolls with breaker bars which are suitable for hard friable materials. The output can be estimated as between $\frac{1}{4}\frac{TWS}{1728}$ and $\frac{1}{3}\frac{TWS}{1728}$ ft³/minute where T is the width of the gap between rolls in inches, W the face width in inches, and S the peripheral speed of the rolls in inches per minute.

Fig. 12   Kibbling rolls

Fig. 13   Cubing rolls

Fig. 14   Double-roll Crusher with Breaker Bars

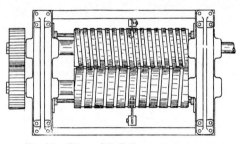

Fig. 15   Grooved Rolls for removing stones

Corrugated rolls or rolls with a helical groove, Fig. 15, are used for the more plastic clays since the corrugations give a cutting action so breaking down the plastic clays more readily. If the clay contains stones the larger stones ride on the top of the helix and are discharged at the end of the roll. Conical rolls having a helical groove are also used for removing smaller stones.

The two rolls are mounted horizontally on a heavy cast iron or steel framework and in almost every machine the bearings of one roll are fixed whilst the bearings of the other roll are spring loaded to prevent damage if tramp iron or other hard material should pass through the rolls. The spring-loaded roll is adjustable with respect to the fixed roll so that the size of the crushed product can be regulated. The two rolls are usually coupled together by gears so that both rolls rotate at the same speed. The main drive is usually by flat belt or V-belt since the flexibility of this type of drive reduces the shock loads on the driving motor when hard or large pieces pass through the rolls.

There are many modifications of these designs, including compound crushers which consist of two or more sets of rolls, one set directly above the other, the upper set through which the clay first passes being the primary crusher and the lower set being smooth secondary rolls which complete the crushing operation.

When the crushing rolls are of the same diameter and rotate at the same speed, which is usually the case in primary and intermediate crushers, the breaking of lumpy or rock-like fragments is done by crushing force alone, but if the rolls are of different diameters or are driven at different peripheral speeds the clay particles are crushed by being drawn between the rollers and are also subjected to the tearing action of friction and rubbing between the clay and roll.

Single-roll Crushers: Single-roll crushers are used extensively in the heavy clay industry for the crushing of clay or shale. They are more extensively used in America where single-roll and double-roll crushers are used in about equal numbers. The single-roll crusher consists of a box frame with a crushing roll having teeth or flutes, different designs being available to suit different materials. The breaker plate or shoe may be fixed or may oscillate by means of an eccentric shaft driven by spur gear from the breaking roll shaft as shown by Fig. 16. Narrow slots in the shoe provide clearance for the long feeder teeth while allowing the breaker plate to be set close up to the roll to prevent oversize. The oscillating breaker plate gives improved efficiency, the output of the machine being increased by about 20 per cent, and choking of the machine is effectively eliminated.

Fig. 16 Single-roll Crusher

Swing-hammer Mills: Hammer mills may be used for breaking down friable materials such as medium-hard clays and shales. They are impact mills and the clay to be crushed falls from the feed box and is hit by the hammers which are rotating at high speed. Some of the clay is broken by impact with the hammers which then fling the clay at high speed against hard steel anvils fitted to the housing. On impact with the anvils the clay is again broken up and the larger and harder pieces bounce back again and are

17

again struck by the rotating hammers. The clay inside the casing is there-fore moving in all directions and a great deal of crushing is done by the impact of pieces of clay against each other without contacting the anvils. A hammer mill of this type is shown by Fig. 17. Since crushing is by impact and the mill has no screen there is no control over the product size except by alteration of the speed of rotation. Thus if the speed is set to break the largest pieces in the feed to $1\frac{1}{2}$ to 2 inches size there will inevitably be a large proportion of the product which is much finer.

Fig. 17   Swing-hammer Mill

Clay Cleaning: The larger impurities in clays should be removed before preparation commences. In the case of clays or shales that are won dry, large stones, tramp iron, pieces of timber or large roots and other impuri-ties which can be readily seen are usually picked out by hand either at the clay pit or on a picking belt. Iron if present can also be removed by means of a magnetic head pulley on a belt conveyor or belt feeder, or it may be removed by an overband magnet, Fig. 18, or by magnetic chute. Usually a magnetic head pulley on a belt conveyor or feeder is the cheapest and most satisfactory way of removing magnetic iron from clay.

In the case of plastic clays it is not easy to pick out impurities by hand and usually they cannot be detected because they are coated with plastic clay and so have the appearance of solid pieces of clay. Machines have therefore been developed for removing stones, roots, etc. from plastic clay.

18

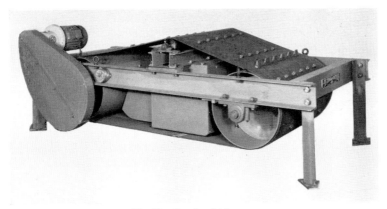

Fig. 18   Overband Magnet

Any impurities small enough to pass these machines, or in the case of dry clays and shales any which pass the pickers, will be ground fine enough in the preparation plant to be uniformly distributed throughout the mix.

Mention has already been made of the use of helical fluted rolls for the removal of stones from plastic clay. Another type of machine developed on the Continent is shown by Fig. 19. In construction it is similar to a pug mill with a perforated barrel and a mouthpiece which is normally closed by a sliding gate valve. Clay is fed into the feed box and is forced into the barrel by rotating knives which cut and mix the clay and force it to the end of the barrel. Not being able to escape through the mouthpiece, the clay builds up a pressure in the barrel and is extruded through the perforations. Any stones which are too large to pass through the perforations are forced along by the rotating knives into the mouthpiece from which they are discharged from time to time by opening the gate valve. When all the stones have been discharged the valve is closed again and only clean clay escapes through the perforations. The cleaned clay is collected on a belt conveyor for transfer to the grinding plant.

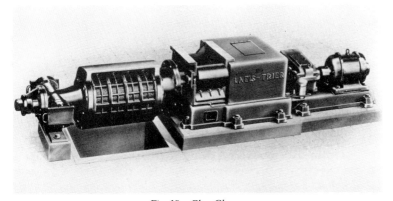

Fig. 19   Clay Cleaner

Clay Shredder: Another way of preparing soft clay for the grinding plant is to cut it into shreds in a clay shredder. Such a machine is illustrated by Fig. 20 and consists of a stationary cylindrical hopper to which baffle bars are attached. A rotating base has slots into which are fitted cutting knives

19

which are adjustable and can be arranged to cut the clay into shreds from $\frac{1}{32}$ inch to $\frac{1}{2}$ inch in thickness. The shreds fall through the slots on to a rotating collector disc from which they are ploughed off by a stationary scraper. Stones are not cut by the knives and so all stones bigger than the shred thickness collect in the hopper from which they can be removed from time to time.

Fig. 20   Clay Shredder

A German machine working on the same principle is illustrated by Fig. 21. In this machine the lumps of clay to be shredded are fed into a conical drum having slots fitted with adjustable cutter knives. Two fixed slotted back-pressure plates press the clay downwards against the knives. The shavings fall on to the rotating collector plate and are continuously discharged by one, or two, fixed ploughs.

Another type of clay shredder is suitable for plastic material which is free from stones. The machine consists of a cylindrical screen trough with a solid bottom and collector plate. The upper portion of the screen trough is of solid steel plate and the lower portion consists of eight screen plates. The whole of this trough rotates about a vertical axis, being driven by spur gears. A central vertical shaft carries the stirring and scraper arms, as shown by Fig. 22. In working, the screen trough rotates but the central shaft, with its arms, is held stationary by means of a pawl. Clay is fed into the trough in which it is mixed by the stirring arms and forced through the

20

Fig. 21   Clay Shredder

Fig. 22   Clay Shredder and Kneader for plastic clay

screen on to the collector plate. A discharge plate cleans both the screen
and the collector plate and discharges the shredded clay to the next operation. Because of this action the clay is well mixed and kneaded and because
of the rubbing action some grinding is effected. When work is completed,

the pawl retaining the central shaft is released and the shaft then rotates with its arms owing to the drag of the clay. Then since the arms and the trough are rotating at the same speed there is no further shredding and the scraper plate cleans the outside of the screen and collector plate. The machine is then stopped.

Secondary Grinding: Primary crushers are only necessary when the clay as won contains large pieces such as is generally the case when it is won by blasting, by power shovel, bucket excavator or by dragline. If it is won by multi-bucket excavator, by shale planer or by scraper, the clay is shaved off the face in small pieces and a primary crusher is not usually necessary. Such clays can be fed directly to a secondary grinder.

The majority of clays in this country are won dry and the most popular type of secondary grinder is the dry pan, its popularity being attributable to its simplicity and ability to cope with a wide variety of clays.

3 : Secondary Grinding of Dry Clays

Dry Grinding Pans: The dry pan is essentially a secondary grinder, and was never intended to break down large pieces of hard material, but it is such an accommodating machine that it is often given the job of grinding pieces of hard clay bigger than it was ever intended to grind but it does it at the expense of increased power consumption, higher maintenance costs and lower output.

The modern dry pan consists of two massive end-frames between which a rotating pan is mounted on a vertical driving shaft. The tops of the end-frames are coupled by a bridge which carries the gearing necessary to drive the pan. The vertical drive-shaft, carrying the pan, rotates in a journal-bearing at the top and a footstep-bearing at the bottom. The runners are two heavy rollers, of large diameter, frequently termed mullers, set on edge, parallel and diametrically opposite to each other in the pan. The mullers are mounted equidistant from the centre of the pan on horizontal axes, which are either connected together or carried on independent arms pivoted about a fulcrum attached to the end-frames.

That zone of the pan base which is in the track of the mullers is fitted with renewable grinding plates, or dead plates, of hard, wear-resisting cast iron or steel. The remainder of the pan base, outside the grinding plates, is usually built up of renewable perforated plates, or grids, through which the ground material passes. Ploughs and scrapers, set close to the grids, direct the material under the mullers.

Operation of the Dry Pan: The material to be ground is fed into the rotating pan and the ploughs and scrapers direct it onto the grinding plates over which the mullers are rotated, by friction with the material, in a plane perpendicular to the plane of rotation of the pan. When the material has passed under the mullers, the rotation of the pan causes the crushed material to be thrown, by centrifugal force, across the grids. That material which is fine enough passes through the grids out of the pan, the oversize being again fed onto the grinding plates by the scrapers.

Grinding and discharging are therefore continuous and to obtain maximum output the feed should also be continuous; thus automatic feeders are essential.

The feed to the dry pan should be controlled by the output from the screens if the best results are to be obtained. If the feed to the pan is maintained invariably constant, then if the feed size varies, although the output from the pan is continuous, the rate of discharge must vary because all pieces are crushed by the same rollers and if at one time there is an excess of large pieces in the feed the rate of discharge must be lower than when the majority of the feed consists of small pieces. It may be thought that it doesn't matter if the rate of discharge does vary because the ground clay is stored in the dust loft or hoppers where there is ample reservoir to look after variations in the rate of grinding; but that is not the point. If the grinding and the grading are to be controlled the conditions in the pan should be maintained reasonably constant. That is, the size of the feed should not vary too widely and the depth of material in the pan should be kept reasonably constant. If there is too much clay or shale in the pan the fines get trapped between the larger pieces and are not discharged quickly enough; they are then returned under the rollers again where they get further grinding and so there is a tendency to get an excess of fines. Furthermore the large pieces lie on a bed of fines and it's like trying to crack a nut on a feather bed with a sledge hammer, it just won't crack and consequently the rate of grinding is reduced. If, on the other hand, there is insufficient material in the pan slightly oversize pieces get into the grid but don't pass through. The grid is thus choked and the fines cannot escape. Some of the oversize pieces are forced through the grid by the scrapers and in any case as soon as they can pass through the grid they do so. Hence if there is insufficient material in the pan there is an excess of both fine and coarse material and a deficiency of intermediate sizes. If therefore the pan is sometimes overcharged and sometimes undercharged there must be a variation in grading analysis which in itself may be a cause of variation in the finished brick.

The weight of the runners must be sufficient to fracture the largest piece over which they pass. For a 9-foot-diameter pan the runners are usually about 60-inch-diameter and weigh from 3 to $3\frac{1}{2}$ tons each, although heavier runners have been fitted for crushing particularly hard material. In some designs the effective weight of the runners is supplemented by additional loads applied by means of a piston in a hydraulic or pneumatic cylinder, acting on the axis of the runner or on the arm which carries it. By varying the applied pressure, the effective load can be adjusted to suit the material being crushed.

Other things which will affect both the output and the grading are the condition of the grinding plates and runners, and the total area of the holes in the grids. If the runners are worn hollow in the centre they cannot grind effectively.

The modern way of maintaining runner tyres in good condition is to face the tyres with hard facing welding rod as soon as the wear becomes appreciable. Hard facing welding rods may also be used to reclaim worn scrapers and ploughs.

The scrapers and ploughs must also be maintained close to the grid plates in order to avoid damage due to tramp iron and to clear the grids of oversize material. If these scrapers are to be set close, the grid plates need accurate fitting in order to obtain a level flat surface. A more modern scraper is the spring-loaded scraper shown by Fig. 23.

Grid plates are usually of cast iron or cast steel. In the casting process

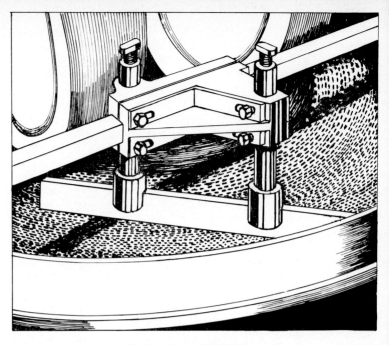

Fig. 23   Spring-loaded Scraper

the stresses set up in the metal as it solidifies and cools are very large and so the holes cannot be very close together, or there is danger of the plates cracking during cooling. Further, unless the holes are opened out with a drill there is the additional risk that some of the holes may be blind. If instead of cast grid plates, the grids are made from steel plate with drilled tapered holes there is no risk of cracking and consequently the holes may be much closer together so increasing the number of holes and thus increasing the screening area which results in a bigger throughput. At a works in Germany where a mixture of clay and colliery measure shale was being ground in an 11-foot dry pan fitted with steel grids having $\frac{5}{32}$-inch-diameter holes, the total area of the holes in the grids was almost twice the total area of the holes in cast plates and the output was correspondingly greater, 12 to 13 tons per hour. The ground material was not screened again but was fed into a hopper from which it was continuously discharged at a constant rate through a rotary feeder into a single-shaft mixer where water was added and then through a pair of high-speed rolls, set close, to a de-airing pug making perforated bricks by the wire-cut process.

At a British works making stiff-plastic facing and common bricks from a colliery shale three 10-foot-diameter dry pans are used. Two of these have the normal cast grids but the third has been fitted with steel grids $\frac{3}{4}$ inch thick with $\frac{3}{16}$-inch-diameter drilled holes (Fig. 24). As in the case of the German grids the total area of the holes is about twice the area of the holes in the cast plates and the output from this pan is said to be 16 tons per hour whilst the other pans which are identical except for the grids have an output of only 7 tons per hour each. Each pan feeds to its own vibrating screen of $\frac{1}{4}$-inch-square mesh so there are practically no tailings returned to the pan with the $\frac{3}{16}$-inch holes, and it has been suggested that the screen can

24

be dispensed with. Not only is the output from the pan more than doubled but the life of the grids is said to be twice as long as cast iron grids, 12 months against 6 months.

Typical Cast Grid.

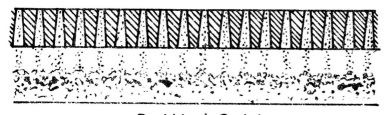

Drilled Grid.

Fig. 24 Typical Cast Grid and Drilled Grid

Although at these two brickworks screening is not necessary, it does not prove that it would be satisfactory in every case particularly if the clay or shale is likely to be sufficiently moist to cause blinding. With some clays the small grid holes may produce too many fines so upsetting the packing density. However the fact that the steel grids with small diameter holes have a so much greater output, and that the ground material needs no further screening, makes it all the more desirable to investigate this problem further for each individual clay and shale.

Various types of perforations have been used in an effort to increase the throughput so that as well as round holes the perforations may be in the form of straight slots, chevrons or S shape.

The speed of the pan is also important because output also depends upon speed of rotation. Thus if we have two identical pans, one running at normal speed and one at half normal speed, the slower running pan will have approximately half the output of the faster pan. This is because the material is fed under the runners only half as many times in any given period. It may have been noticed that during the past 20 years there has been a tendency for pan speeds to increase. For example pans which formerly ran at 23 to 24 r.p.m. now run at 28 to 30 r.p.m. and even faster. The upper limit of speed is governed by the effectiveness of screening by the grid plates. If the speed is too high the ground material is flung right across the grids to the rim by centrifugal force and then is ploughed back again across the grids to the runners at too high a speed to be properly screened. For this reason pans with inclined grids Fig. 25 can run at a higher speed than those with flat grids because the inclination of the grids tends to slow down the material as it passes over them. Again rim-discharge pans because they have no grids can be run at a still higher speed.

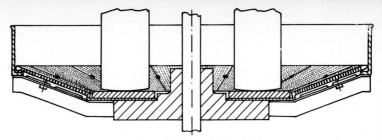

Fig. 25   Dry Pan—Inclined Grids

The size of the largest pieces that will pass under the runner depends upon the angle of nip, which differs for different materials, according to the following relationship:

$$d = D \tan^2 \frac{\theta}{2}$$

where d=diameter of the largest piece that will pass under the runner

    D=diameter of runner

    θ=angle of nip.

The angle of nip may be defined as the greatest angle that will draw the material to be crushed between the two converging faces.

Generally the harder the material to be crushed the smaller the angle of nip. Thus, if the diameter of the runner is 60 inch, and the angle of nip is 20 degrees, then the largest piece that will pass under the runner will be 1·86 inch, but if a softer material having an angle of nip of 40 degrees is to be ground, the largest piece that will pass under a 60-inch-diameter runner will be about 8 inch diameter. (Fig. 26.)

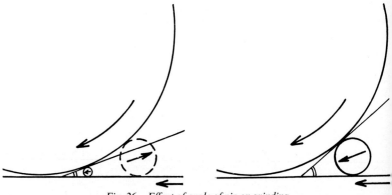

Fig. 26   Effect of angle of nip on grinding

One thing which must be remembered however is that the effective angle of nip is reduced as the speed is increased so that the higher the speed of the pan the smaller must be the size of the feed. This can be seen in any pan which is charged with large pieces. During normal running some of the large pieces may not pass under the runners, but if the pan is stopped it will be seen that, as the pan slows down, these large pieces will pass under the runners and be crushed. Whilst therefore a low-speed pan will deal with a larger feed size than a higher-speed pan, the output will be less for a normal size of feed because the material is not passed under the runners so frequently.

26

This therefore brings us back to where we started—the necessity for passing large size feed of hard material first through a primary crusher, and because the discharge is continuous the feed should also be continuous. **Types of Dry Pans:** There are two main types of dry pans, generally known as open-base pans and underscraper pans.

In the former, the ground material is discharged into a large hopper, usually excavated in the floor, and thence into the boot of a bucket elevator which feeds the grading screens. In the case of the underscraper pan the material discharged through the grids falls onto a collector plate, which generally rotates with the pan, from which it is ploughed off at a fixed point by a stationary scraper into the boot of the elevator. In some designs the collector plate is stationary, and scrapers attached to the underside of the rotating pan drag the ground material round until it is discharged through an opening in the collector plate.

Mention has been made of the rim-discharge pan in which there are no grids. The whole of the pan base is solid. A stationary rim surrounding the rotating base is adjustable so that the gap, or opening between the edge of the pan and the rim, can be adjusted to regulate the size of ground product to pass through. The ground clay is thrown by centrifugal force to the outside of the rotating pan and that which is ground small enough passes through the gap onto a collecting disc below from which it is ploughed off to the boot of a bucket elevator which takes it to the screens. With this type of pan since the ground clay escapes through a continuous gap, which is kept clear of oversize material by scrapers which return it to the grinding track, the pan speed can be higher than for a gridded pan, and the output is considerably greater in spite of the fact that the circulating load is also usually higher. A diagram of the rim-discharge pan is shown by Fig. 27.

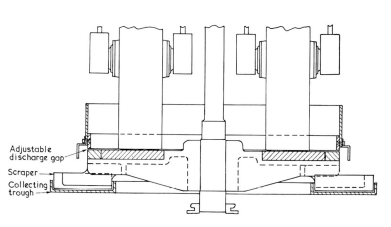

Fig. 27   Rim-discharge Pan

Secondary Hammer Mills: Secondary hammer mills are similar in principle to the primary hammer mills already described but are designed to produce a finer product. Whilst the primary crushing hammer mill has an open base the secondary grinding type is fitted with a screen as shown by Fig. 28. These machines are not very popular in the heavy clay industry in this country because there is no control over the grinding except by speed variation and they tend to produce an excess of fines. In the U.S.A. they are more frequently used particularly for the grinding of the tailings from the screens instead of returning them to the pan mill.

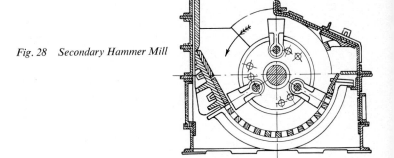

Fig. 28   Secondary Hammer Mill

Disintegrators: These are a form of double-roller mill used for breaking up clays and shales; they consist of two rolls rotating in opposite directions within a casing. One roll, a smooth roll, is larger in diameter than the other which is fitted with knives, breaker bars or corrugations. The large smooth roll rotates at a much lower speed than the other and serves to feed the clay between the two rolls. The breaker roll rotates at high speed and the difference in speed, together with the action of the knives, bars or corrugations, disintegrates the clay to a size suitable for feeding to a final set of high-speed rolls to complete the grinding. A typical disintegrator is shown by Fig. 29. This particular machine has a chilled cast iron smooth roll 24

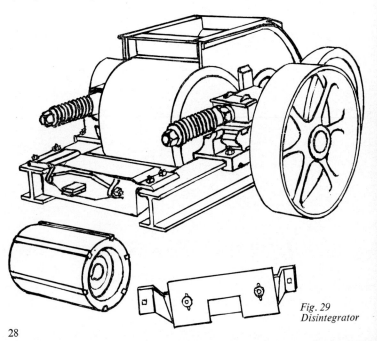

*Fig. 29
Disintegrator*

inch diameter by 18 inch wide which rotates at 50 to 60 r.p.m. and a small chilled cast iron roll 13 inch diameter by 18 inch long fitted with six hardened steel cutting bars which rotates at 700 to 800 r.p.m. Springs are provided to allow the large roll to give way if an uncrushable object falls into the machine. Such machines are used where the material is hard and lumpy. The rolls are adjusted as close together as possible and the resulting action on the material passing through the machine shreds it very fine, breaking up small stones and throwing out large ones. The machine has an output sufficient for 5,000 to 12,000 bricks per hour, depending upon the clay and the speed. A similar machine having rolls of the same diameter but only 12 inch long has an output of 2,000 to 6,000 bricks per hour.

Such machines are not in general use in this country but they are used extensively in the U.S.A.

Attrition Mills: Attrition mills are being used in the heavy clay industry particularly when fine grinding is essential. They are sometimes used in conjunction with a pan mill for the grinding of the screen tailings. Many clays contain hard impurities which are difficult to grind in a pan mill and the removal of these from the pan greatly increases its output. The pulverization of the tailings reduces them to a fine powder and renders them innocuous so that they may be remixed with the ground clay so improving the appearance, colour and strength of the brick. The harmful effects of limestone and iron-stone both of which are quite common constituents of building brick clays are thus eliminated.

(a) **Atritor Mill:** This machine is shown in section by Fig. 30. It consists of a hopper, into which the clay is fed, below which is a rotary disc feeder by means of which the rate of feed can be regulated by adjusting the position of the scraper on the disc.

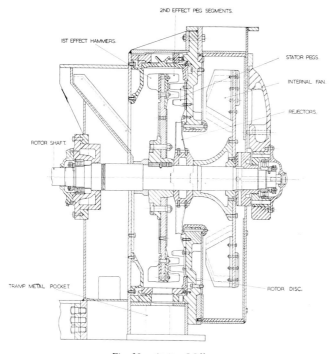

Fig. 30   Atritor Mill

From the rotary disc feeder the clay passes down a chute into a pulverizing compartment where it is subjected to the disintegrating effect of hammer segments. This reduces the size of the material to such an extent that it can be carried over the periphery of the rotor into the attrition zone by the conveying air. In this zone the movement of the particles is most complex. They are carried inwards towards the centre by the air stream and outwards again by the action of the rotor. The fixed pegs facilitate and accelerate the creation of vortices and prevent gyration of the dust cloud with the rotor. The intense turbulence created in this zone causes the particles to collide and to rub together so that grinding is effected by attrition of the particles against each other.

When the particles have become superfine they are carried by the air stream out of the turbulent zone to the centre eye of the fan impeller which then ejects them with the exhaust air. Closely adjacent to the eye of the diaphragm, which separates the pulverizing and fan compartments, is a rejector consisting of one or more spoon-shaped arms, rotating with the shaft, which return any oversize particles to the pulverizing zone.

The air drawn through the machine by the fan may be heated to dry the material in the machine and since the Atritor contains only a few pounds of material at any moment, all of which is in circulation, an enormous surface area is exposed to the drying influence of the hot air. The hot air may be obtained from a coke or oil fired stove or as waste heat from the kiln.

The ground material is collected in a cyclone collector.

(b) **Pin Disc Mill:** This mill consists of a rotor fitted with beaters which rotate between pins attached to a stator and is illustrated by Fig. 31. The material to be ground is fed to the mill through a hopper which directs it to the centre of the mill. The rotating beaters in the centre hit the feed and fling it outwards by centrifugal force where it hits the first row of stationary pegs on the stator, so breaking by impact. That material which is fine enough to pass between the pegs is picked up by a second row of beaters on the rotor which flings it outwards to a second row of fixed pegs on the stator. In this zone grinding is accomplished by percussion and attrition. The beaters on the periphery of the rotor keep the ground material in violent agitation until it is fine enough to pass through the control sieve surrounding the rotor. The material which has passed through the sieve is discharged through an opening in the base of the mill.

Such machines are rarely used in the heavy clay industry in this country but they are to be found on the Continent and in the U.S.A.

The size of the finished product can be controlled by the spacing between the pins in the stator and by the speed of rotation of the rotor.

Impact Mill: A type of mill used sometimes in the U.S.A. and now being manufactured in this country is illustrated diagrammatically by Fig. 32. The material to be ground enters through the inlet onto the surface of the spinning rotor and rapidly slides out between the top and bottom plates in a thin even stream. The row of impactors at the periphery of the spinning rotor then strike each particle with full shock of impact, thus shattering and accelerating the material to a high velocity. The particles, having acquired high kinetic energy, then shatter themselves against stationary impactors in the target area thus achieving further particle size reduction. The average particle size of the ground product is controlled by the speed of the rotor, thus the higher the speed the finer the product, and since the crushing energy is imparted to the material by virtue of its velocity, which is constant, a narrow band width of particle sizes is obtained.

Fig. 31   Pin Disc Mill

Fig. 32   Impact Mill

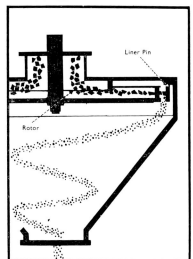

4 : Screening and Grading

Materials ground dry are screened to remove oversize pieces from the ground product. The oversize rejected by the screen is returned either to the same or to another grinding mill for further grinding.

For the manufacture of bricks the clays do not need to be very finely ground although the grinding mills do produce variable particle sizes, from fines to the largest fragments which will pass through the mill. This is desirable in order to obtain the desired packing density and to reduce porosity, since with a variable size of product the fines will pack between the coarser grains. The coarse grains should however not exceed a certain maximum which will depend upon the nature of the clay being used. The screen is therefore intended only to take out the oversize.

Several types of screen are available, the following being the most important.

Stationary Screens: These are the simplest type of screen used in the industry and consist of an inclined screen mounted on a suitable frame. The angle of inclination is adjusted to suit the material being screened but is usually about 45 degrees. Various types of screen deck are available, the simplest being a perforated steel sheet. Perforated steel can be obtained in standard sheets 6 feet, 7 feet and 8 feet long by 3 feet and 4 feet wide in 16-, 18- and 20-gauge with holes ranging from $\frac{1}{16}$ inch to $\frac{1}{2}$ inch diameter. The sheets are available with the holes of square or staggered pitch, the latter having more holes per screen and therefore a larger screening area. Perforated plate screens are simple and rarely suffer from blinding if the angle is correctly adjusted because those pieces which are only just small enough to pass through the perforations tend to jump across the holes due to their momentum in rolling down the screen. The screen therefore only passes particles which are smaller than the size of the perforations. As the larger particles jump over the perforations they carry with them some fines which ought to pass through the screen. For this reason the perforated plate screen is not particularly efficient, and a certain amount of fine material is returned to the mill with the tailings.

Specially shaped perforated steel stepped-plate screens shown by Fig. 33

Fig. 33   Stepped Plate Screen

induce a riddling effect on the material passing over with a rapid elimination of fines. The tapered holes prevent pieces getting wedged. These stepped screens may be used as either stationary or shaking screens.

Piano-wire screens consist of a rectangular frame, which slopes at an angle of about 45 degrees, over which wires are strung from top to bottom of the frame and stretched taut in the same way as the wires on a piano frame. The wires are made of a special toughened and tempered steel to withstand the high tensile stress to which they are subject when tightened. There are no cross wires and the fines fall through the gaps between the wires while the coarse material slides over the top. The objections to the piano-wire screen are that wedge-shaped pieces tend to force the wires apart so that larger particles are passed through and owing to the resulting extra tension in the wires, and the additional abrasive wear, the wires break. For these reasons the screens need frequent inspection.

An improvement on the piano wire is the use of wedge wire screens. Wedge wire was first manufactured in Germany but is now made in various designs in this country. Wedge wire with a flat top has the advantage that once a particle enters the aperture it will drop away without danger of clogging. If the wedge is made with a ridged top in place of the more common flat top, the fine material is guided towards the slots by the slanting sides of the ridges while the coarse material rides on top. Wear due to the passage of material over the screen is mainly confined to the top of the ridge which can wear down without affecting the accuracy of the mesh, resulting in a longer useful life of the screen.

Square top wedge wire allows the screen to wear down the full depth of the parallel-sided portion before the slot width begins to increase at all, thus increasing the life of the screen but at the expense of reduced screening efficiency on account of the greater risk of clogging in the parallel portion of the slot.

The three types of wedge wire screen are illustrated by Fig. 34. Owing to the shape of the wire these screens have a very high mechanical strength and can be supplied with slot widths in all sizes from $\frac{1}{16}$ inch to 2 inch.

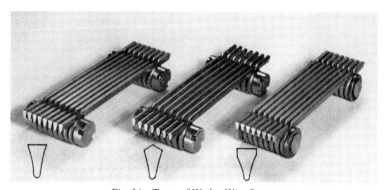

Fig. 34   Types of Wedge Wire Screen

Rotating Screens or Trommels: Rotating screens consist of cylindrical or truncated conical screens mounted on a central shaft by means of spiders at each end. In the case of the cylindrical screen the shaft is inclined at a small angle to the horizontal and the ground product to be screened is fed into the interior of the cylinder at the higher end. In the case of the conical screen the shaft may be horizontal and the ground material is fed in at the small end. As the screen rotates the material is pulled up by the rotation and rolls down the screen from the high end to the lower end so that in effect it traverses the screen in the form of a spiral. The screens are usually made of perforated sheets although sometimes they are made of wire mesh. To prevent blinding of the screen, nylon or bristle brushes are mounted on a freely rotating shaft with the brushes in contact with the top of the screen as shown by Fig. 35. As the screen rotates the brushes also rotate thus keeping the screen clear. An alternative method of cleaning is to have a driven shaft over the screen to which leather thongs are attached. These thongs beat the screen plates and the vibration set up by this shakes the screen clean. The output from rotary screens is small, only about 0·06 tons/hour/square foot of screen area, because less than 25 per cent of the screen area is effective.

Fig. 35 Rotating Screen

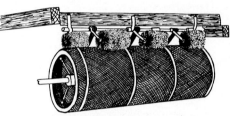

Vibrating Screens: Vibrating screens may be mechanically or electrically vibrated. Mechanical screens are vibrated by means of (1) an out-of-balance pulley, (2) an eccentric, (3) a cam or hammer.

In the first of these the screen is mounted in a frame which is flexibly connected to a rigid support, usually by springs, which allow the screen frame to vibrate. Such a screen is illustrated by Fig. 36. Rigidly connected

Fig. 36 Vibrating Screen—Out-of-balance Pulley

to the screen frame are bearings which carry a shaft fitted with an out-of-balance pulley. The amount of out-of-balance can be adjusted, the greater the out-of-balance the larger the movement of the screen. The amplitude may be adjusted from about $\frac{1}{32}$ inch to $\frac{3}{16}$ inch. The motion of the screen is slightly elliptical and the rotation of the pulley should be such that the top of the pulley moves in the opposite direction to the travel of material on the screen. The speed of rotation is about 2,000 r.p.m. for large screens and up to 3,000 r.p.m. for small screens. The screens are inclined usually at an angle of about 37 degrees but the correct angle for any particular material should be found by trial.

The positively-vibrated type of screen Fig. 37 is one in which the vibrations are caused by an eccentric shaft. It consists of three essential parts, the supporting frame, the screen body and screen deck, and the driving mechanism. The body is usually of steel side plates suitably stiffened with angles and arranged to carry one or more screen decks as required. This body is suspended on the driving mechanism, which consists of an eccentric shaft running in ball or roller bearings, in such a way that the screen body is suspended from the eccentric portion of the shaft while the concentric part runs in bearings carried on the main frame. The main frame can be suspended by suitable wires and springs from a supporting structure or be bolted down to a foundation with springs or rubber buffers to prevent the transfer of vibrations to the foundation. The eccentricity and speed of the eccentric shaft vary for different materials and product size but for screening dry ground clay the eccentricity is about $\frac{1}{32}$ inch which gives a rotary screen movement at all points of $\frac{1}{16}$ inch.

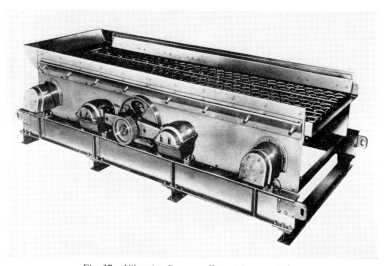

Fig. 37   Vibrating Screen—Eccentric operated

The third type of screen which is operated by cams and hammers is illustrated by Fig. 38. In this type the screen angle is usually about 45 degrees and the screen cloth is stretched taut on a frame by springs which maintain a strong and uniform tension on it. Above, extending right across the screen, are arranged a number of shafts each carrying a series of cams or cranks which lift, at rapid intervals, a corresponding number of hammers

35

which are allowed to fall freely on to the upper ends of pins which are connected at their lower ends to the screens. The screens are struck at rapid intervals causing vibrations of small amplitude to be set up in the taut screen.

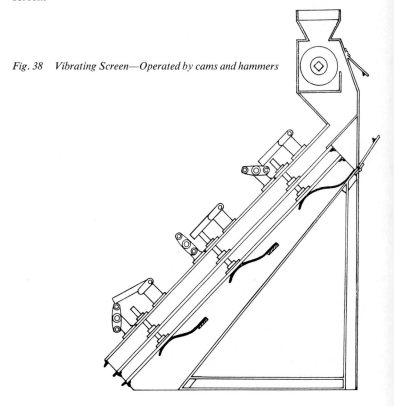

Fig. 38   Vibrating Screen—Operated by cams and hammers

If two or more screens are used, one above the other, to separate the material into separate grades, the pins are carried through and connected to all the screens so that they vibrate in unison.

There are several variants of these three basic designs but of these the most interesting is probably the resonance screen. By vibrating the screen at its natural frequency a high degree of vibration is built up by the application of small impulses at appropriate intervals. The power consumption of such screens is extremely small. Conventional vibrating screens which usually operate at more than twice their natural frequency pass through the resonance frequency both during starting and stopping and unless they pass through this frequency quickly excessive vibrations occur.

The resonance screen works at a very low angle, almost horizontal, and the screen body is supported by laths or flexible cantilever supports inclined at 30–45 degrees to the vertical so that the direction of motion, which is at right angles to the supports, is 30–45 degrees to the horizontal depending upon the application. The screen is shown diagrammatically by Fig. 39 in which the vibrating screen frame (a) is supported on the base frame (b) by means of the cantilevers (c). The amplitude of vibration is limited by the buffers (d) which consist of metal lugs securely fixed to the screen frame which contact soft rubber buffers at each end of the stroke. The gaps

36

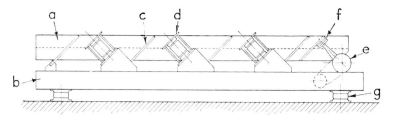

Fig. 39   Resonance Screen

between the lugs and the rubber buffers are adjustable so that the stroke can be regulated. When the lugs contact the soft rubber, the rubber is compressed so storing up energy which is released when the screen comes to rest so forcing it back in the opposite direction. Most of the energy required to operate the screen is obtained from this source, the only energy to be supplied by the driving motor being that which is lost in friction and that which is required for actually conveying the material along the deck. The drive is by means of an eccentric (e) and connecting rod attached to the screen frame through a soft rubber buffer (f). The base (b) is supported on soft rubber buffers (g) with no metal connection to the supporting structure. This eliminates vibration of the supporting structure or building.

Gyratory Screens: These screens work horizontally and gyrate in a horizontal plane by means of an out-of-balance flywheel so that all parts of the screen mesh move in horizontal circles of about $\frac{3}{16}$ inch diameter. The original speed of rotation of the out-of-balance flywheel was 1,000 r.p.m. but speeds have now been increased up to 3,000 r.p.m. The gyratory screen was developed during the war for screening highly explosive powders and has since been used for other materials. The throughput of these screens is exceptionally high and blinding is considered to be almost impossible.

A modification is the 'Rotex' screen, Fig. 40, which is flat and nearly level, the normal angle of inclination being 4 degrees. The screen frame has an almost level gyratory motion that varies from a full circular motion at the head end to a reciprocating motion at the discharge end. Blinding is prevented by bouncing rubber balls below the screen mesh.

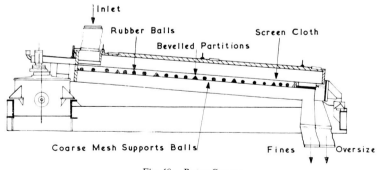

Fig. 40   Rotex Screen

Electrically Vibrating Screens: High-speed electrically vibrated screens are used mainly for fine screening. The electro-magnetic vibrator is mounted directly over the screening surface, as shown by Fig. 41, and the vibrations generated by it are transmitted directly to the screen cloth while the body

Fig. 41   Hummer Screen

of the screen remains stationary. Usually the normal 50 cycles supply is passed through a metal rectifier, to obtain half-wave rectification, so that pulses of direct current are applied to the vibrator to give 3,000 vibrations per minute to the screen cloth. In some cases a lower frequency is desirable and then a frequency changer, or motor generator set, is provided to supply current at the desired frequency.

Heated-mesh Screens: One of the biggest troubles with wire mesh screens is due to the blinding of the mesh by moist clay. It has been found that this blinding is not so much due to the total water content of clay as to the surface film on each of the particles. When a particle of clay touches a wire, the surface film of water adheres to the wire and the surface tension of the water tends to support the particle. Particles which are thus supported can be removed by excessive vibration such as by beating the screen, or by forcible removal as by brushing, or by preventing the adhesion of the water film to the wire mesh so that it cannot support the weight of the particle. This latter method can be achieved by heating the wire mesh to a suitable temperature, depending upon the feed rate, moisture content, mesh size, etc. If this is done there can be no adhesion of the water film on the surface of the clay particle so that no superficial tension is built up in it to support the particle. Maximum throughput and maximum screening efficiency is thereby obtained, thus reducing the power consumption of the pan mill and the elevator.

The simplest way of heating the screen mesh is to insulate it from its supporting frame and to pass low voltage electricity through the mesh. Heat is generated in the wires of the mesh by the passage of electric current through the screen wires themselves. The voltage applied across the screens is about 10 volts and the current flowing should be sufficient to maintain a screen temperature of about 40 degrees C., but this temperature depends upon the clay and the water content. The actual amount of current necessary to produce this temperature depends upon the size of the screen, the metal of the wire and the diameter of the wire. The power input to the screens is approximately equivalent to the load removed from the pan and elevator.

The advantages of electric heating are claimed to be:

1. All labour at the screens eliminated except for periodic inspection.
2. Increased life of screen.
3. More efficient screening resulting in a smaller amount of tailings being recirculated.
4. Less wear and tear on mullers, grinding plates and screen plates in dry pan.
5. Because the rejects are usually harder stone-like particles they contain less moisture than the softer clay particles which pass through and this has the effect of slightly increasing the moisture content of the through-put.
6. Since the heated mesh prevents adhesion of clay to the wire mesh, it is possible to effectively screen clays having a moisture content that would clog up an unheated screen.

Grading: A significant change takes place in the grading analysis when using a heated-mesh screen. Because of the higher efficiency the recirculating load is less than with an unheated screen and consequently less re-grinding of particles that should pass through the screen, but do not, is required. This results in the finer fraction becoming significantly less. In order to restore the grading analysis it may be necessary to make some alterations to the conditions in the mill.

Tests on a Heated-mesh Screen: Tests on an 8 feet by 3 feet 10-mesh single-deck live-wire screen showed that, without heating, the screen needed to be cleaned every 10 to 45 minutes depending upon the water content of the clay. On starting up, the efficiency of screening was 96 per cent, but after 25 minutes' running with a clay of 7·6 per cent to 8·2 per cent water content the screening efficiency had fallen to 25 per cent.

A heated-mesh screen did not need to be cleaned even after five months' continuous running and the efficiency of screening remained practically constant. The power consumption for heating this screen was 7kW which is rather less than 0·3kW per square foot of screen area.

5 : Wet Grinding and the Grinding of Plastic Clays

The grinding of wet and plastic clays is usually carried out in a wet pan followed by smooth high-speed rolls, although other types of machines of the disintegrator type have been developed and are being used quite extensively particularly in the U.S.A.

Wet Pans: In construction the wet pan is somewhat similar to the gridded dry pan already described, the main differences being as follows.

In the dry pan the pan rotates and the axes of the mullers are stationary whereas in the wet pan the pan is stationary and the mullers are rotated about the vertical axis.

In the dry pan the mullers are at the same distance from the centre and diametrically opposite to each other. They run on a solid, flat, annular grinding track. In the wet pan the mullers are frequently at different distances from the centre so that the tracks of the two mullers cover the whole of the area of the pan base. Either the whole of the pan base is perforated or there may be one or more solid grinding plates to grind any hard pieces in the plastic clay mass. The number of solid grinding plates to be used depends upon the nature of the clay being ground and in some cases may even be more than half the area of the pan base. The face width of the mullers is usually greater than for the same diameter of dry pan and their action is both to grind the clay and to force it through the perforations over which it passes. Ploughs rotate with the mullers and these fold the clay in the pan over on to itself in order to improve the mix and to attempt to get a more uniform product.

A typical wet pan is illustrated by Fig. 42.

Fig. 42   Wet Pan

The perforations in the base of the wet pan are usually in the form of slots which vary in size from about 4 inch by $\frac{3}{8}$ inch to about 10 inch by 1 inch according to the nature of the clay and the output required. With such large slots some coarse material is bound to be forced through with the clay and

40

so it is usual to regrind the product from the pan mill through one or more sets of smooth rolls, each set progressively closer together, until the final rolls are usually high-speed rolls, set close, running at differential speeds.

If the clay does not contain sufficient water in the raw state, and generally although it may be plastic it requires more water to be added, the additional water is added in the wet pan. This is usually added through one, or two diametrically opposite, radial perforated pipes attached to an annular container surrounding the central shaft into which water flows continuously at the rate required. Since the perforated pipes rotate with the central shaft the water is added more or less uniformly over the clay in the pan.

Disintegrator: A disintegrator for plastic clays is somewhat similar to the disintegrator used for dry clays and consists of a large-diameter smooth roll which rotates at a low speed and a smaller-diameter toothed roll, the teeth sometimes being of the swing hammer type, which rotates at high speed. The large smooth roll serves to feed the clay into the gap between the rolls where it is disintegrated by the teeth on the high-speed roll. On some machines there is an additional curved disintegrator plate which maintains the clay in contact with the high-speed teeth for a longer time, so improving the tearing action.

Mud Hog: This is an American machine, now made in this country, and is of the swing hammer type having a series of moving anvils as indicated by Fig. 43. The anvils are coupled together in the form of a slat conveyor passing over a heavy steel anvil frame, to reduce shock, and any clay which adheres to the anvils falls off as it passes round the lower wheel. Since there are a large number of anvils, their life is comparatively long and the hammers on the rotor are reversible. The machine can be used for dry or moist plastic clays.

Fig. 43   Mud Hog

Smooth Rolls: These consist of two smooth rolls mounted on horizontal spindles carried in bearings on a heavy cast iron or steel frame. Low-speed smooth rolls are usually coupled together by gears, the main drive being by flat or V belts driving onto a pulley on one of the shafts. In the case of high-speed rolls, however, the two rolls are driven independently by belts usually at speeds differing by about 10 per cent. Typical high-speed rolls are shown by Fig. 44. The two rolls are usually of the same diameter, the most popular size being about 30 inch diameter, and the speed of rotation for the higher-speed roll is such that the peripheral velocity exceeds 1,000 f.p.m., and is more usually 1,500 f.p.m., and for fine grinding finishing rolls may reach 2,000 f.p.m. Thus for 30-inch-diameter high-speed rolls the speeds may vary from 130 to 250 r.p.m. with the slower roll running at 115 to 225 r.p.m. Low-speed rolls usually both run at the same speed and in these machines the breaking down is done by crushing force alone. In the case of differential speed rolls the clay particles are broken down by combination of crushing and the tearing and rubbing between the clay and the rolls.

The capacity of smooth rolls in cubic feet per minute varies somewhat according to the nature of the material being ground but it can be estimated as $\frac{3}{4}\frac{TWS}{1728}$ ft³/minute where T is the distance between rolls in inches, W the width of the roll face in inches, S the peripheral speed in inches per minute.

To retain efficiency of grinding, roll faces must be kept true and for this purpose a grinding attachment should be provided to grind up the roll faces in position. The abrasive nature of clay tends to cut fine grooves in the surface of the rolls and it is when these grooves appear that the surface should be reground. The frequency of grinding therefore depends upon the nature of the clay being ground but it is usually necessary to true up high-speed rolls about once a week although some may require more, and others less, frequent grinding.

High-speed rolls are set very close together, often as close as 0·020 inch apart, and the axes are fixed to give this setting, there being no spring loading.

Fig. 44   High-speed Rolls

6 : Mixing and Tempering

Having ground the clay the next step is to thoroughly mix or blend the clay in order to obtain a consistent body and then to temper the clay with water. Tempering does not mean the mere addition of the correct amount of water but also involves the equalizing of the moisture distribution throughout the whole of the clay mix.

The mixing of dry powders is comparatively easy. If done as a batch process it may be carried out in a tumbling drum, mixing cone, muller or pan mixer, or by a ribbon mixer. In the heavy clay industry it is more usual to use continuous machines and the types most generally used are trough mixers, ribbon conveyor mixers, continuous drum mixers and pan mixers.

The mixing of heavy pastes and dough-like materials such as the mixing of plastic clays is the most difficult of all the mixing problems encountered in the heavy clay industry. This also may be a batch or continuous process but the most popular machine in the industry is the double-shafted trough mixer.

Mixing Dry Powders: For batch mixing the double-cone blender, Fig. 45, or the tumbling box, Fig. 46, are both suitable machines. In the double-cone blender the powder is tumbled against the sloping walls so that its disposition is constantly changed and rapid mixing is effected. In the tumbling box the powder falls against the sloping sides and is thrown from one end of the box to the other and this also effects rapid mixing.

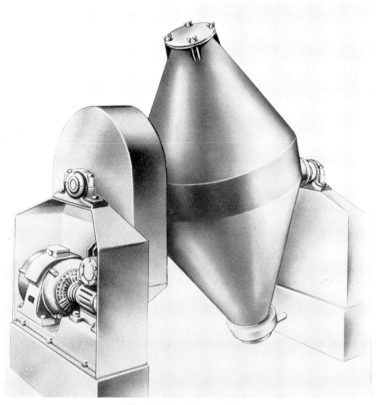

Fig. 45 Double-cone Mixer

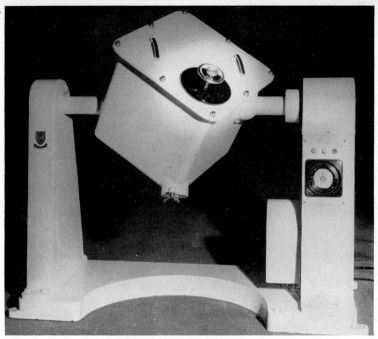

Fig. 46   Tumbling Box Mixer

The tumbling drum consists of a horizontal cylinder rotating about its axis. On the inside of the periphery of the drum are fitted scoops or lifter plates which lift some of the material and cause it to cascade over the remaining powder in the drum. This also effects a rapid mix. The pan-type mixer consists of a rotating pan on which are rotating blades mounted on an axis which is offset from the pan axis as shown by Fig. 47. The blades rotate at a higher speed than the pan and the mixing action is obtained from the scroll motion of the blade round the pan as indicated by Fig. 48,

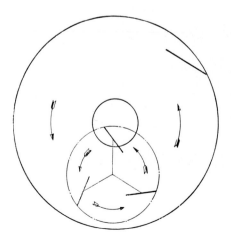

Fig. 47   Rotating Pan Mixer

Fig. 48   Action of Rotating Pan Mixer

The ribbon mixer consists of a horizontal 'U' shaped trough fitted with a horizontal shaft with spiders, to the ends of which are fitted left- and right-hand spiral ribbons of steel as shown by Fig. 49. During rotation the ribbons not only cause lifting and cascading of the material but also by their spiral form cause the material to be thrown alternately to the right and to the left, thus effecting more rapid mixing, the material being discharged at the centre.

Fig. 49   Ribbon Mixer

For continuous mixing the outer spirals of the ribbon mixer are all of the same hand and the inner spirals are of the opposite hand. With ribbons of the same width the outer spirals sweep a bigger volume of powder in one direction than the inner spirals do in the opposite direction. There is therefore a continuous flow from one end of the mixer (the feed end) to the other end (the discharge end) at each revolution of the shaft equivalent to the difference in the volumes swept by the inner and outer spirals. The blades of such a machine are shown by Fig. 50, the material being fed in at one end and discharged at the other end.

Trough mixers are also used for continuous mixing and these are all modifications of the screw conveyor. For example in a normal screw conveyor running in a trough the mixing action can be improved by fitting flat blades between the helices of the screw, the blades being inclined in the

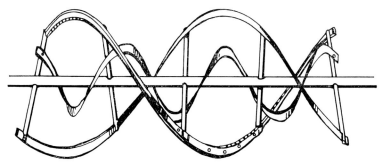

Fig. 50   Blades for Continuous Ribbon Mixer

opposite direction to that of the screw. Also by suitably notching the flights of the screw and turning the ends back to form scoops, or by the fitting of rakes, good mixing of dry powders is obtained.

By far the most popular mixer in the heavy clay industry is the single-shafted trough mixer which consists of a horizontal shaft fitted with flat blades all inclined in the same direction running in a 'U' shaped trough. The materials to be mixed are fed in at one end and the rotating blades lift and cascade the material over itself giving the mixing action and at the same time, because of the inclination of the blades, cause it to be propelled along to the discharge end. Machines of this type are very good mixers of dry material or of moist material that will not ball up. They are frequently used for tempering but are not so satisfactory for this purpose owing to the tendency for the wetted clay to roll up into balls which are wetter inside than outside.

Mixing Plastic Clays: For the efficient mixing of plastic clays cascading is not sufficient. It is necessary to cut the plastic pieces and to knead them. Two types of trough mixer are suitable for this purpose. The first is the conventional double-shaft mixer, Fig. 51, in which two horizontal shafts fitted

Fig. 51   Double-shaft Mixer

with overlapping knives rotate in opposite directions in a double 'U' shaped trough. The knives cut the plastic clay pieces, cascade them over and on to each other, and then as the knives come together in the centre a certain amount of kneading is done. The knives on both shafts are inclined to propel the clay from one end of the trough to the other where it is discharged so that the machine is a continuous mixer. The other type of machine has a short trough in which are two horizontally mounted overlapping 'Z' type blades which rotate at the same speed, or more usually one rotates at twice the speed of the other. This type of machine is not popular in the heavy clay industry, probably because it is a batch machine, although it is very widely used in other industries which work in plastic materials. A development of this machine, so far made only by German manufacturers, has converted the machine into a continuous mixer and shredder, Fig. 52, and in this form it is now being used in German heavy clay works and is known as a Siebkneter. One half of the trough is made of solid steel plate and the other half of perforated steel plate. The blades are so designed that,

46

in addition to the cutting and kneading action, the clay is propelled slowly from the solid to the perforated end of the trough where it is rubbed through the perforations by the rotating blades. In this way the machine becomes continuous in action, the plastic clay being fed in at the solid end and discharged in shreds at the perforated end.

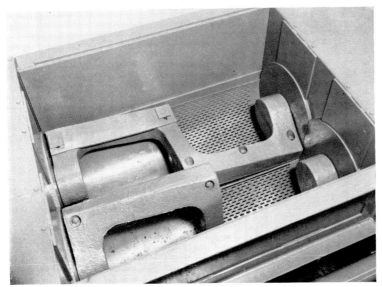

Fig. 52   Continuous Dough Mixer—Siebkneter

The 'Maukmixer' is a pan mixer which is usually mounted immediately below and concentric with an open-base wet pan. The clay from the wet pan falls directly into the mixing pan so that clay is being continuously received over its whole area. The mixing pan, Fig. 53, is intermittently

Fig. 53   Maukmixer

rotated by ratchet and pawl mechanism to rotate at about 6 r.p.m., although this speed is adjustable. The pan is discharged by a continuously rotating screw which may discharge at either the centre or the periphery of the pan on to a belt conveyor.

Tempering: Tempering machines may also be of either batch or continous type, although the continuous method is generally preferred. As a general rule no special machine is installed for tempering, the necessary water usually being added in the grinding plant or mixer. Thus for semi-dry-pressed bricks the water is added at the dry pan, for stiff-plastic bricks it is usually added in the mixer, whilst for wire-cut bricks it depends upon the clay and the method of preparation. Thus if the clay or shale is ground in a dry pan the water is usually added in a mixer or if ground in a wet pan the water is usually added in the pan. If the water is added as early as possible in the process the subsequent preparation machines help to give a uniform mixing of the water throughout the clay and the time between the addition of the water and the actual shaping allows a period for soaking.

If a trough mixer is used for tempering it has already been noted that a double-shaft mixer is considered to be better than a single-shaft mixer because in the latter there is a tendency for the wetted clay to ball up collecting the drier clay on the outside. These balls of clay can frequently be seen travelling along the mixer without being broken up. In the double-shaft mixer there is a certain amount of cutting and kneading which tends to produce a more uniform water distribution.

Another type of machine sometimes used is a mixing pan with pug mill combined (Fig. 54). In some districts this machine is known as a tempering

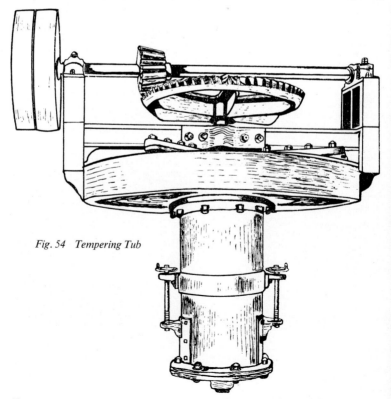

Fig. 54   Tempering Tub

tub and in some others as a sludge pan. It consists of a shallow pan about 7 feet diameter to the base of which is attached a vertical pug. A central vertical shaft carries four radial arms fitted with mixing blades and scraper knives which mix the clay and water in the pan and feed it to the centre into the vertical pug. The central shaft continues through the full length of the pug mill and in this section carries pug knives which cut and knead the clay and force it downwards to the discharge opening in the side at the bottom of the pug barrel.

Pan mills are also used as tempering machines. The normal tempering pan consists of a solid-bottom revolving pan, fitted with two mullers mounted on a stationary horizontal shaft, and fixed ploughs to fold the mix over and direct it under the mullers. The mullers are frequently suspended slightly clear of the pan base so that their action is that of kneading the clay as it passes under them. Water is added as required and the machine is run for a definite time until the tempering is considered satisfactory. Discharge is by lowering a scoop into the pan which scoops up the clay and discharges it over the rim of the pan. A pan of this type showing the scoop in the discharging position is shown by Fig. 55. During the tempering process the scoop is raised.

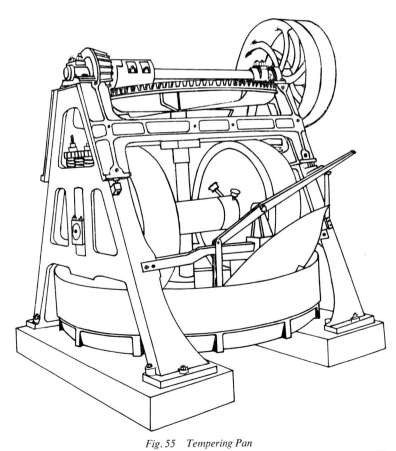

Fig. 55   Tempering Pan

Another design of tempering pan has a fixed solid-bottom pan and rotating mullers and ploughs. This is also a batch machine and the principle of operation is exactly the same as the rotating pan machine. On completion of tempering the clay is discharged through a gate valve in the bottom of the pan. The face of the valve is flush with the bottom of the pan and it is operated by means of a screw. A portion of the face of the mullers passes over the opening so forcing the tempered clay through the opening when the valve is opened.

Whatever method of tempering is adopted it is desirable to add the water in the form of a fine spray over as large an area as possible in order to obtain a uniform distribution. If the water is added by means of a perforated pipe some particles of clay are inevitably wetter than others and if added through an open-ended pipe, as is still so often the case, there is bound to be a considerable variation of water content throughout the mix unless the plastic mass is thoroughly mixed and kneaded after the water has been added.

Steam Tempering: Reports of tests carried out on the steam treatment of clay have shown that the plasticity and mechanical strength of the green ware is generally improved. Tests reported from Western Europe, U.S.A., and U.S.S.R. all indicate that difficult clays are rendered more workable and less sensitive to drying, in fact steam treatment has been likened to de-airing in that it decreases the air absorption and increases the hydration of the clay minerals. It has been stated that good results have been obtained, during experiments, with clay heated by steam to a temperature of 35 degrees C. but that more marked advantages would have accrued if the temperature of the clay had been higher. Modern industrial practice is to heat the clays with steam to a temperature of 70 degrees to 80 degrees C. and occasionally, on particularly difficult clays, to 90 degrees C. Once the clay has been heated it is essential that it should not be allowed to cool, but its temperature should be maintained throughout the shaping and drying processes. It is suggested in a U.S.S.R. report that the temperature should be maintained for at least 20 minutes before shaping and, since the breakdown of many clays begins only after 20 minutes of steam treatment, a longer treatment time is desirable.

Steam treatment increases the moisture content of clay mixes by about 3 to 5 per cent, so that clays with high moisture contents cannot be steam-treated unless they are previously dried or grog is added. For the drier mixes the addition of cold water should be about 3 to 5 per cent less than the final moisture requirement so that the additional moisture may be added as steam. A European report suggests that with steam heating the final moisture content for satisfactory shaping may be 2 to 3 per cent lower than for cold shaping.

The main improvements of steam tempering are the better workability of the clay, which results in a better extruded column, and the avoidance of preliminary drying, so avoiding rejects due to cracking during this stage of drying. It is also claimed that steam tempering reduces laminations and 'dog earing' and also reduces the power required for extrusion by about 20 per cent. Drying times are considerably reduced depending upon the temperature of shaping and setting in the dryer: drying times of half the normal drying time have been reported.

7 : Feeders and Storage

Since brickmaking is a continuous process with intermediate storage at strategic points, automatic feeders are desirable.

At some works hand feeding is still practised but this increases the number of man hours and so increases the cost of manufacture. At some other works clay is fed to the pan mill intermittently by tipping a tub of clay into the pan and then when the pan is almost completely empty another tub of clay is tipped in. It has already been pointed out that this practice results in inefficient utilization of the pan mill, gives a variable grading analysis and increases maintenance.

To work efficiently machines which have a continuous output should have a continuous feed, the two being equal to maintain constant operating conditions in the machine. The only way to obtain a constant feed is to use continuous mechanical feeders some of which will now be considered.

The type of feeder used depends a good deal on the type of material it is to feed. Also in order to be able to give a constant feed it must have a constant, or a bulk, supply from which to draw. For example clay as won at the clay pit is not delivered at a constant rate. It is usually brought in rail tubs, lorries or dumpers and so the supply is intermittent. This intermittent supply has to be evened out and this is done by means of a surge bin which is a steel, concrete, or brick hopper, into which the clay is tipped, fitted with an automatic continuous discharge which is capable of being regulated to suit the requirements of the next machine. A box feeder is therefore a type of surge bin, and consists of a rectangular chamber of one or more compartments fitted with an intermittently moving slat-conveyor base operated usually by a pawl and ratchet. This type of feeder is suitable for feeding lumpy clay to a primary crusher, or crushed clay or plastic clay to a secondary grinder. If plastic clay is fed by a box feeder it is necessary to have a rotating digger as shown by Fig. 56 in order to get a constant discharge rate. Other types of surge bin may have a screw discharge or a reciprocating discharge. In the latter case the bottom of the bin is made to oscillate forwards and backwards with a stroke which is adjustable. On the forward movement the material to be ground is carried forward and on the backward movement the unground clay drops off the feeder into a chute leading to the grinder.

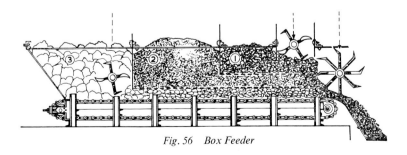

Fig. 56   Box Feeder

A type of surge bin suitable for dry ground clay is a rectangular hopper fitted with a Moore Bin Discharger shown by Fig. 57. This consists of a rectangular steel hopper fitted with an open base consisting of steel angles,

6 inch by 6 inch, set apex upwards with a clear space of about $2\frac{1}{2}$ inch between the bases of adjacent angles. Specially shaped fins, having parabolic sides about 3 inch wide at the base, fit between adjacent angles throughout the base. All the fins are mounted on a common holder which is adjustable in the vertical direction so that the fins may be in any position between the angles to give fully closed, fully open or any intermediate position between, and the holder to which they are attached is fitted to an electric vibrator which vibrates all the fins at a frequency of 3,000 cycles per minute. The amplitude of vibration is controlled by a rheostat. Vibrating the fins fluidizes the dry ground clay and effectively prevents arching. The clay discharged falls into the receiving hopper, fitted with a drag-link conveyor, and thence is discharged at one end. The discharge hopper is fitted with a level controller and if the hopper fills to a certain fixed level the vibrator is automatically switched off and then when the level has fallen it is automatically switched on again. A further manual control is obtained with a slide over the discharge opening from the drag-link conveyor. These dischargers are extremely useful for dry or semi-dry ground materials which normally tend to arch.

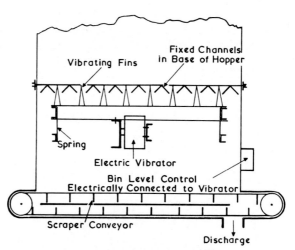

Fig. 57   Moore Bin Discharger

Rotary disc feeders, Fig. 58, are popular for feeding dry or semi-dry ground clays to tempering machines or presses. Frequently they are attached to hoppers in which case the bottom of the hopper is fitted with a vertical discharge tube below which is a rotating disc. The clay falling through the feed tube forms a cone on the rotating disc and an adjustable stationary scraper ploughs off the required amount of clay. The feed tube may be central with the disc or may be off-centre. In the latter case there is no need for the discharge scraper to extend into the feed spout to remove the material because the material is drawn out of the spout by the movement of the revolving disc.

52

Fig. 58
Rotary Disc Feeder for dry ground clay

Another rotary disc feeder which is fitted with a cylindrical hopper and is kept charged by a conveyor is illustrated by Fig. 59. A stationary cylindrical hopper having an opening in the side has a rotating disc base and a fixed adjustable scraper which ploughs the clay from the rotating disc at a constant rate.

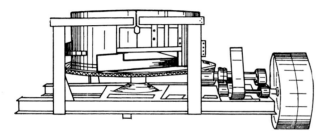

Fig. 59   Rotary Disc Feeder for plastic clay

Plastic clay does not discharge satisfactorily from the plain rotary disc feeders just described, but by modifying the type shown in Fig. 59, by the addition of a central vertical shaft carrying a three-bladed arm cross fitted with scrapers which rotate with the base, satisfactory feeding is obtained. Such feeders are used for feeding prepared plastic clay direct to pugs.

Another type of feeder for ground plastic clay consists of a vertical cylindrical screen made of perforated plate attached to a stationary base plate. A central vertical shaft carries a four-armed cross fitted with blades of such shape that as the shaft rotates the clay is forced through the perforations on to a rotating circular table from which it is ploughed off by a stationary scraper. The outer collecting table rotates in the opposite direction to the internal mixing arms. This machine as well as being a feeder also mixes and shreds the plastic clay so that it is in a condition to be fed directly into the pug.

The rotary vane feeder, Fig. 60, is also suitable for feeding dry ground clay from hoppers to tempering machines or mixers. Although the feeder is not strictly continuous the capacity of each pocket is comparatively small, and they each discharge in turn, so that the effect is almost the same as a continuous feeder. If the clay is moist there is danger of the pockets not emptying.

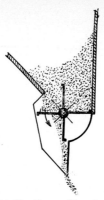

Fig. 60   Rotary Vane Feeder

Vibrating feeders are often used and these are very similar in construction to vibrating screens except that a solid deck is substituted for the screen mesh and the angle of throw is modified to give a conveying action. Vibrating feeders may be horizontal or inclined, and the vibrations may be set up mechanically by means of an out-of-balance pulley or by an eccentric. Electrically vibrated conveyors of the type shown by Fig. 61 may also be used as feeders.

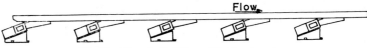

Fig. 61   Electrically Vibrated Feeder Conveyor

Constant Weight Feeder: The constant weight feeder, Fig. 62, as its name implies, delivers material through an automatically regulated weighing mechanism. The weighing mechanism consists of a continuously moving rubber-covered endless belt conveyor with short centres, so mounted that it pivots on knife edges at or near the centre line of the head or discharge pulley. The other end of the conveyor, the tail end, is supported on scale

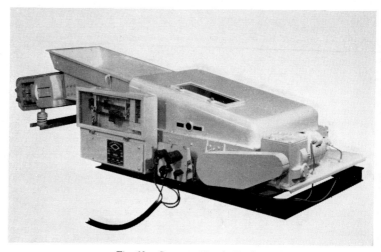

Fig. 62   Constant Weight Feeder

levers, which together with calibrated beams and adjustable weights constitutes the scale which is also fitted with electric controls to indicate over or under weight. The signals from this are transmitted to a control box or relay which automatically controls the amplitude of the vibrating feeder, or the opening of the gate, which controls the feed rate.

The constant weight feeder will deliver a continuous uniform flow of a given weight per hour and the rate may be changed to any other value between maximum and minimum by merely changing the position of the counterpoise on the scale beam.

The machine actually weighs the amount of material on the weigh belt at any time and since the belt runs at constant speed the weight indicated is a measure of the feed rate. Actually the weight of material per foot length of belt times the belt speed in feet per minute gives the weight of material per minute.

By the incorporation of an automatic time switch it may be used for batch weighing.

For cleanliness in dealing with dry materials the feeder and weigh belt are enclosed in a dust-proof casing.

8 : Soft Mud Method of Shaping

Although clay preparation consists mainly of grinding, mixing and tempering the clay, the type of machines used depend upon the nature of the clay. For certain types of clay, and for certain methods of production, grinding may be dispensed with. Such a process is the soft mud process used in the Stock Brick industry.

In the Stock Brick industry the clays are invariably surface deposits of fine texture and are won either by hand or by mechanical excavators. The clay and water are fed into a large circular tank called a wash mill where a slurry is formed by slowly rotating harrows or wash gates, and impurities are washed out; heavy impurities such as stones and pebbles sink to the bottom, light impurities such as timber and roots rise to the top. Chalk or lime is also made into a slurry, in a similar wash mill, and may be mixed with the clay slurry and be pumped together into the settling tanks or wash backs. Chutes are used to distribute the slurry over the wash backs to minimize segregation and effect some mixing. The water is allowed to drain away and town refuse is laid on the top. In the wash backs the heavier particles of clay settle quicker than the lighter ones so there is a tendency for the bottom of the clay to be of coarser grain size than the top. For this reason the clay is won from top to bottom, starting at one end, and loaded into trucks or tubs for transfer to the making plant.

The brickmaking machine illustrated by Fig. 63 is a form of pug mill with rotating knives working in a cylindrical barrel to force the clay along from the feed box to the other end where the barrel or cylinder is somewhat enlarged and has discharge openings in the periphery at the bottom. The end of the barrel is closed. Fitted to the shaft, over the discharge openings, are spiral shaped blades or spatulas which force the clay through steel dies into sanded moulds immediately below. The moulds may be sanded by

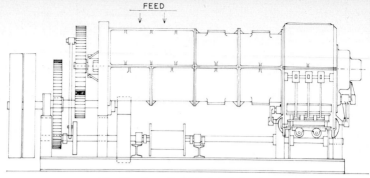

FEED

Fig. 63 Berry Soft Mud Brick Machine

hand or automatically and may be fed to the machine by hand or automatically. They are however fed into position under the discharge openings and pushed out again on the other side of the machine automatically. The moulds are knocked against a stop on the table to loosen the bricks and then inverted so that the bricks drop out on to a table where they are handled between thin wooden boards and set on pallets, the moulds being returned for re-sanding. Drying is in car tunnel dryers or in hacks. The process is simple, there is not a great deal of machinery but there is a great deal of handling, and manual handling is expensive so that the more the process can be mechanized the better.

In America where there always appears to be the urge to 'keep things moving' resort has been made to the continuous ball mill. The wet bank clay is fed to a ball mill by means of a granulator-type feeder which granulates the clay and feeds it at a constant rate to the ball mill. Water is added in just the correct amount for use in the brickmaking machine, sometimes less but in this case soda ash is used as a deflocculant to make the clay more fluid. This, it is said, reduces shrinkage and consequent drying loss, and increases the dry and fired strength. Sometimes however, the clay as won is too wet and then lime is added.

In this process the ball mill is not used as a grinder but rather as a mixer in which dispersion of the clay particles in the water is effected. Any grinding which does take place is purely incidental. The clay is in the form of soft mud and although not fluid is highly thixotropic so that it behaves as a fluid when in the mill. From the mill the material is screened and fed through a double-shaft mixer to the brickmaking machine. The process is therefore continuous. This process does not appear to have been used in this country but the advantage of the process is that being continuous the discharge from one machine is the feed for the next and so less handling charges are involved. The disadvantage is that there is no buffer stock between the raw clay and the brickmaking machine.

In some districts wash mills and wash backs are not used. For example, in Essex no chalk is added because there is already sufficient lime in the clay. The clay is sometimes prepared in wash mills and drained in wash backs, as already described, but sometimes it is prepared in wet pans followed by mixers and rolls before being fed to the brickmaking machine. In Kent, chalk is prepared in the wash mill and drained in the wash back; the prepared chalk is added to the raw clay in a wet pan, where water is added,

56

and then through mixers and rolls to the brickmaking machine. If the raw clay is too wet, hydrated lime is added as well as chalk.

The American machine is somewhat different in design as shown by Fig. 64. It consists of a single- or double-shaft feeder which delivers the clay to a vertical pug. Another design is somewhat similar but is fitted with a horizontal pug.

Fig. 64   Lancaster Soft Mud Brick Machine

With these machines the pockets of the moulds are automatically sanded, the moulds are fed under the press to receive their charge of clay, surplus material is automatically 'struck off', the strikings are retained in the press box, automatic bumpers loosen moulded shapes in the moulds and automatic dumpers deposit the formed shapes onto pallets and return the empty moulds for re-sanding.

An automatic pallet car loader is available for use with these machines. In operation four pallets, loaded with bricks, collect on an accumulator table. At the front of the table runs a rail track for the dryer cars with a lowering and elevating section. As soon as four full pallets are on the accumulator table they are automatically pushed forward on to the lower shelf of the forward part of the dryer car. An operator then presses the push button of the electric control which lowers the dryer car one shelf, and the next batch of four pallets is fed forward on to the dryer car. The dryer cars are 10 shelves high and when the top shelf has been loaded the car is pushed forward and the top shelf of the rear half of the dryer car is loaded. The car is then raised shelf by shelf until the car is fully loaded with 80 pallets. The elevating platform is now at ground level and the filled car is taken to the tunnel dryer and an empty car takes its place on the elevating platform.

The brickmaking machines are made in various sizes having maximum outputs of from 7,500 to 15,000 bricks per hour. The moulds are of wood,

57

usually either maple or cherry, with steel reinforcement on the top and bottom faces. The number of bricks per mould is usually from 6 to 10 dependent upon the size of machine used.

9 : The Wire-cut Method of Shaping

The wire-cut method of making bricks is used in most civilized countries of the world. Roughly one-third of all the building bricks made in Great Britain are wire-cut. Common bricks made by this process are extruded, cut to size on a wire-cutting table, dried and fired. Facing bricks are usually rusticated, sand-faced or re-pressed before drying, according to the requirements of the market.

Wire-cut bricks are made from plastic clays and shales which may be won in a plastic condition or, if won dry, are brought to a plastic condition before shaping by tempering with water and by suitable preparation to bring the clay into condition for extruding through a die. The amount of water in the clay body necessary to produce this condition varies with the nature and type of clay being used, but is usually in the region of 15 to 20 per cent.

In order to get clay of this consistency to flow through a die it has to be forced through and there are three accepted ways of doing this. They are the piston extruder, expression rolls, and the screw extruder.

The oldest method of extruding a clay column was by means of the piston extruder, but this is an intermittent process as the piston has to be withdrawn to refill the cylinder with clay. Expression rolls produce a continuous column which is then cut into individual bricks but modern mass-produced wire-cut bricks are invariably produced by a screw extruder.

Screw Extruders: The simplest form of screw extruder consists essentially of a barrel, in which a close fitting, axial screw rotates. At one end is an opening through which the material to be extruded is fed and at the other end is a die or mouthpiece through which it is extruded. There are many pugs of this type still in regular use in the brick industry making good bricks from plastic clay. For the more difficult clays de-airing pugs are now almost universally used. De-airing pugs consist essentially of two barrels with a de-airing chamber between. The first barrel has a feed box at one end and a clay seal at the other end with some form of shredding device which cuts the clay into shreds. These shreds pass into the de-airing chamber and are extruded from the second barrel through a die. The de-airing chamber is sealed from atmosphere by the clay seal on one side and by the sealing of the die at the other end. Four different designs of de-airing pugs are shown by Fig. 65. In this figure (a) and (b) are stepped barrel pugs, sometimes referred to as 'double-deck' pugs, whilst in (c) and (d) the two barrels are co-axial and are referred to as 'in-line' pugs. The principle of operation is the same in each case although the parts are arranged differently.

Fig. 65a shows a conventional double-deck machine in which the lower (extrusion) shaft passes into the de-airing chamber from outside and therefore requires a seal to prevent ingress of air to the vacuum chamber. Fig. 65b shows another type of double-deck machine in which the clay flows from

58

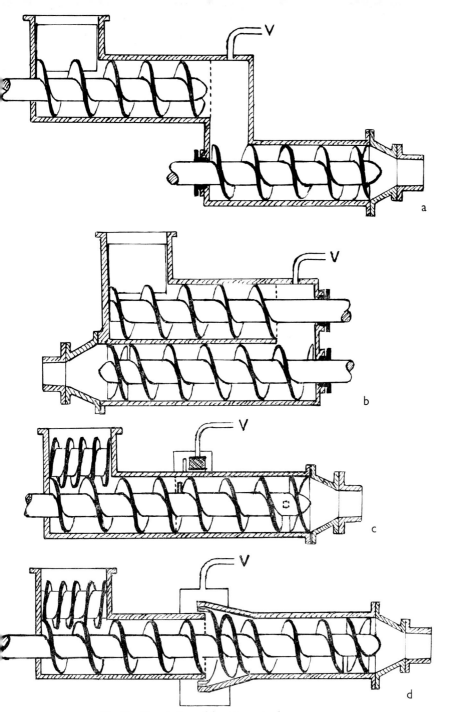

Fig. 65   Four designs of de-airing extruders

left to right in the upper barrel, is shredded into the de-airing chamber, and
in the lower barrel is extruded from right to left through the die. In such a
machine the two shafts pass through into the de-airing chamber from out-

side thus necessitating two seals. The risk of air inleakage is doubled, and maintenance of seals is doubled, but with well designed seals this should not be a very serious matter. On the other hand the floor space occupied is less than with the more conventional type and this may be of far greater importance in certain cases. Figs. 65c and 65d show in-line machines in which the two barrels are in line with the de-airing chamber in the centre. The first auger extrudes the clay through a shredder plate into the de-airing chamber, thus sealing the de-airing chamber from the feed box. The second auger is longer, and usually has a steeper pitch than the first auger in order to get the clay out of the de-airing chamber quickly to prevent this from getting choked. The only difference between the machines shown in Figs. 65c and 65d is the design of the vacuum chamber. In Fig. 65c the vacuum chamber is to one side of the barrel, on that side at which the auger is travelling in a downward direction. Communication between the de-airing chamber and the inside of the barrel is by means of a hooded opening which is open at the bottom facing downwards. There is thus no tendency for the clay to choke the opening in normal working, but if for any reason the second barrel becomes filled and the communication passage does get choked it can easily be cleared by depressing a lever which forces a rod through the opening. In Fig. 65d the de-airing chamber is a concentric chamber outside the barrel and communication is by means of an annular gap, around the outside of the first barrel, formed by the conical beginning of the second barrel. This gap is kept clear by means of two curved fingers which project into the gap and rotate with the shaft scooping out any clay which may have entered.

Apart from these general differences in design there are a large number of variations in the design details of the different parts of the machine. Each machine manufacturer has developed his own ideas with the result that there are probably more different designs of extrusion machines for the making of wire-cut bricks than there are for any other process of brickmaking.

Feed Box: In brickmaking machines which are fitted with smooth rolls over the feed box the clay is fed in a thin ribbon into the feed box and separate

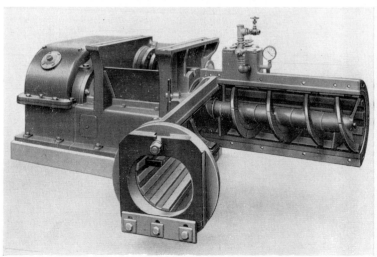

Fig. 66   Keller Extruder with helical feed roll

feed rolls are not necessary. When the pug is fed from a mixer or from automatic feeders, such as belt feeders, slat feeders or circular feeders, and particularly when it is fed by hand there is risk of clay building up on one side of the feed box. In order to prevent this, feed rolls are fitted. Some pugs are fitted with smooth feed rolls, some with fluted rolls and some with helical grooved rolls (Fig. 66). The advantage claimed for the fluted and the helical grooved rolls is that they become filled with clay and so become, in effect, clay rolls. Some pugs have, instead of feed rolls, flat plate or paddle-type feeders.

The modern tendency is however to utilize the feed box as a mixer.

One German manufacturer has incorporated a mixer and kneader of the type generally used for doughs and heavy pastes (Figs. 67 and 68). The mixer consists of two heavy section 'Z' type mixing blades which rotate

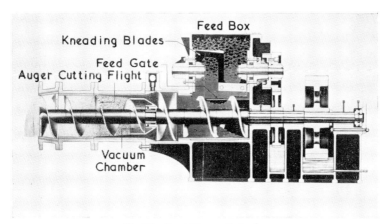

Fig. 67   Soest-Ferrum Extruder

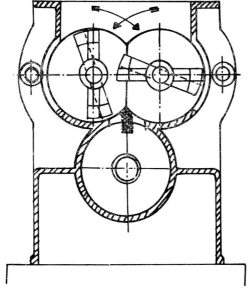

Fig. 68   Section of Feed Box—Soest-Ferrum Extruder

slowly in opposite directions within a housing formed by two semi-circular plates. The gap between the two semi-circular plates can easily be adjusted to regulate the rate of clay-feed to the pug. The clay is subjected to the mixing and kneading action of the blades and is forced through the space between the shutters, for the full length of the mixer. This, it is claimed, consolidates the clay feed, squeezes out much of the air which is entrained, and effectively seals the first auger from ingress of air from outside.

Several manufacturers have extended the feed box to form a single-shaft mixer. Fig. 69 shows the single-shaft mixer incorporated into a stepped barrel (double deck) machine and Fig. 70 shows a single-shaft mixer incorporated into a straight-line machine.

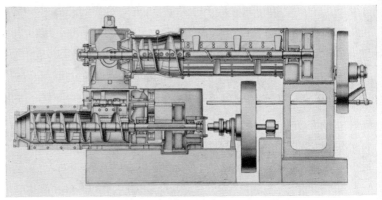

Fig. 69   Section through Weserhütte-Extruder

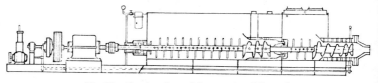

Fig. 70   Section through International Extruder

The incorporation of a double-shafted mixer as an integral part of the shaping machine is not so usual but is done by certain manufacturers, (Figs. 71, 72 and 73), although it has been common practice for a long time to use single- or double-shafted mixers, for tempering the clay mix, feeding directly into the normal feed box.

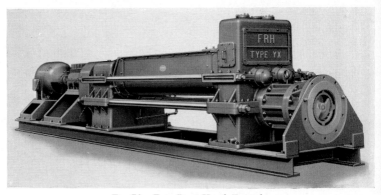

Fig. 71   Fate-Root-Heath Extruder

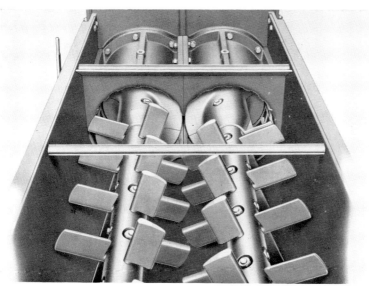

Fig. 72   Feed-box Mixer, Fate-Root-Heath Extruder

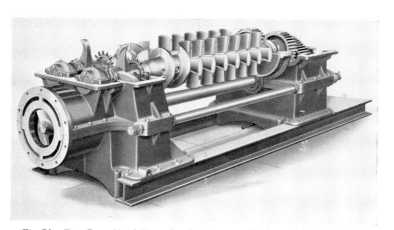

Fig. 73   Fate-Root-Heath Extruder showing mixer blades and shredder knives

De-airing Chamber: The de-airing chamber must be sealed from atmosphere, and at entrance, at the end of the first barrel, the seal is usually made by extruding the clay into the de-airing chamber through a perforated shredder plate. The perforations in the shredder plate are sometimes round holes and sometimes slots. One German pug designer has said that all too often the holes in the shredder plate are too large to allow de-airing to be effective. He claims to have carried out tests which indicate that the thickness of the shreds should not exceed $\frac{3}{8}$ inch. If the holes in the shredder plate are circular then, according to this, they should not exceed $\frac{3}{8}$ inch diameter or if they are slots the minimum dimension of the slots should not exceed $\frac{3}{8}$ inch. The usual dimension of the slots supplied by this designer is $1\frac{1}{4}$ inch by $\frac{3}{8}$ inch.

Usually a rotating cutting knife is fitted to the shaft on the de-airing chamber side of the shredder plate, to cut the shreds into short lengths and this again increases the surface area per unit weight of clay and so helps in the removal of air.

British, Continental and American de-airing pugs can be obtained with shredder plates, but some machines are available with a different method of shredding. This is shown by Figs. 69, 70 and 73. In this method the clay in the first barrel is extruded over a diverging cone, within the barrel at the end of the first auger, so that a concentric cylinder of clay is extruded into the de-airing chamber. This cylinder of clay is shredded by a rotating multi-bladed cutting knife, mounted on the auger shaft, so that the greater the number of cutting knives, the thinner the shreds, and consequently the more effective the de-airing. Fig. 73 shows this method applied to the machine with a double-shafted mixer and twin augers in the upper chamber of the stepped barrel machine. Fig. 69 shows it applied to the more normal stepped barrel machine and Fig. 70 shows it applied to the in-line machine.

Fig. 67 shows an interesting development of the shredding device. In this machine the second, or extrusion, auger starts inside the hollow cone and is increased in diameter as soon as it leaves the cone. The first turn of the auger outside the cone has a serrated periphery which cuts the annular ring of clay, extruded between the cone and the barrel, into small shreds. The air is extracted from inside the cone and if any shreds should be drawn into the cone they are immediately pushed out again by that portion of the auger which is enclosed within the cone.

Extrusion Barrel: Following the de-airing chamber is the extrusion barrel through which the clay is forced by the auger into the mouthpiece and die. In this barrel the clay is consolidated but unfortunately the clay leaves the auger in the form of a spiral. If a double wing knife is fitted, the single spiral formed by the auger is again cut into twin spirals, one intertwined with the other. The aim is to knit these spirals of clay together into a homogeneous column and it can only be done in the spacer and die.

Spacer and Die Design: In some pugs an attempt is made to destroy the structure of the clay by inserting radial pegs in the barrel between the end of the auger and the wing knife as is done in the pug illustrated in Fig. 66. Whilst this destroys the structure set up in the auger, a new structure is developed in the clay as it passes through the wing knife and the clay still enters the spacer as two intertwined spirals.

Unless some other method of destroying laminations is adopted the only thing to do is to correctly design the spacer and die to suit the particular clay being worked. Unfortunately no two clays are exactly alike and so the spacer and die will vary for each individual clay as well as for each individual pug. For this reason there is no formula from which to design them and the only way to get good results is by trial with the particular machine and clay.

Generally speaking the more plastic the clay the longer the spacer required and the shorter the die, and conversely, the leaner the clay the shorter the spacer and the longer the die. If the spacer is too short the laminations generally show up as spirals on the face of the column at right angles to the direction of extrusion and sometimes a definite 'S' crack may be visible. If the die is too long the laminations will be concentric with the outline of the die. Laminations can be made visible by freezing a section of the column, or by evacuating under water for about 1 minute, or by subjecting to a steam pressure of 50 p.s.i. for 2 minutes. The correct design of spacer and die gives an irregular pattern.

64

Sometimes an alteration in the design of wing knife is sufficient to effect a cure. There are however a few clays which do not respond to variations in the design of wing knife, spacer or die. In such cases it is desirable to alter the mix. If the clay is too lean, plastic clay should be added to make it more workable. On the other hand if the clay is too plastic, sand, grog, ashes, ground coke breeze or some other non-plastic material should be added. The correct amount of the addition can only be found by experiment.

For very soft plastic clays a German pug manufacturer has introduced a vibrating grid into the mouthpiece as shown by Fig. 74. The amplitude of vibration must be at least equal to the distance between the wires and the frequency of the vibrations is 3,000 per minute. It is claimed that this device has been used successfully when extruding electrical porcelain, but it would not be suitable for the much stiffer clay bodies used for brickmaking.

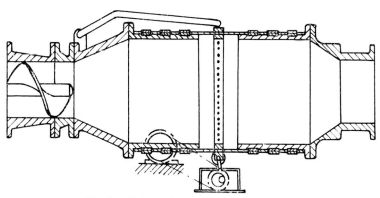

Fig. 74   Reducing laminations—Vibrating Grid

Another suggestion, shown by Fig. 75, is that the main auger shaft should be hollow and inside it an oscillating shaft carries a perforated disc which oscillates at frequencies up to 3,000 per minute immediately in front of the end of the auger. The clay leaving the auger passes through the oscillating perforated disc and the high rate of shear set up develops the thixotropic properties of the clay and tends to make it flow more nearly as a viscous fluid into the spacer and die where its plasticity is restored. This is claimed to have the same effect as the vibrating grid with the consumption of much less power.

Another German development designed to eliminate laminations is shown by Fig. 76. In this device the mouthpiece or barrel is extended and inside it rotates a cylinder of blades. The outlet is at right angles to the direction of extrusion and the blades smear the clay, layer upon layer, into the die.

A considerable number of suggestions have been made for overcoming laminations, and although all may work with particular clays under certain conditions so far no universal cure has been found.

Non-conventional Pugs: With so many variations in the design of conventional machines it is not surprising that several non-conventional machines have been suggested. When clay is extruded from a conventional auger machine the clay leaving the auger is rotating and the spacer has to be made sufficiently long to arrest the rotation before the clay enters the die.

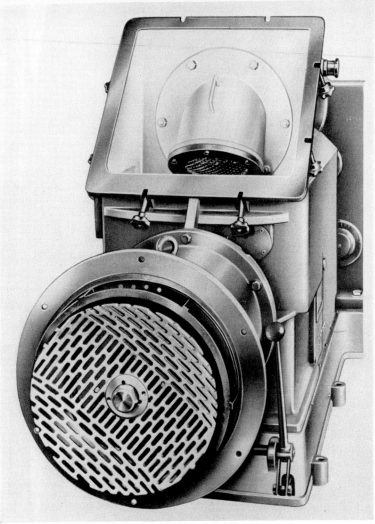

Fig. 75   Reducing laminations—Oscillating Grid

Fig. 76   Reducing laminations—Rotating Blades

To avoid having to do this Dr. Ludovici suggests that the mouthpiece be rotated so that there can be no relative rotation in the die. As an alternative to this he suggests that if for practical reasons the mouthpiece must be stationary then the auger also should be stationary and the barrel should rotate about the stationary auger. Both these designs have been patented but as far as is known no such machines are working on production.

One interesting machine of American design, which is also made in this country, is the Hawk pug (Fig. 77). The clay is fed from a cylindrical mixer into a rotating barrel inside which is a stationary shaft fitted with blades. The barrel revolves in ball-bearings and the shaft is offset slightly (about $\frac{1}{16}$ inch) from the centre of the barrel. The second fixed barrel is larger in diameter than the first barrel and fits over it to give clearance between the outside of one and the inside of the other of about $\frac{1}{32}$ inch. The shaft in the second barrel is attached to the rotating first barrel but also runs $\frac{1}{16}$ inch eccentrically in the fixed barrel. The de-airing chamber encloses the whole of the first barrel and about half the length of the second barrel, and the first barrel is in communication with the de-airing chamber at each end. The clay seal is at the die and at the entrance to the first barrel which is fitted with baffle knives, and is fed by a worm feeder.

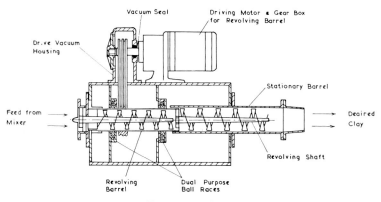

Fig. 77   Hawk Pug

Another machine of non-conventional design is known as the vac-mixer. This machine was designed by L. Walker of Sheffield and Fig. 78 shows it in its original form. The clays are ground, screened, proportioned and mixed dry and are fed into a hopper which feeds the vac-mixer at a constant rate through a rotary valve. The clay falls from the valve on to two baffles which distribute the clay so that it falls through the vertical de-airing chamber in the form of a thin curtain of powder. The de-airing chamber and pug barrel are exhausted by means of a vacuum from the back of the barrel, seals being effected at the rotary valve and the die. Inside the de-airing chamber, just behind the baffle plates, are spray nozzles which project fine sprays of water on to the falling clay particles in the de-airing chamber. The small particles of clay enable the de-airing to be rapid and effective and each particle soaks up its share of water like a sponge. The wetted clay is then extruded through a short barrel and die.

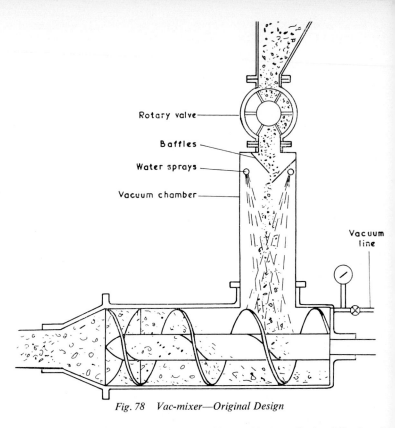

Rotary valve

Baffles

Water sprays

Vacuum chamber

Vacuum line

Fig. 78   Vac-mixer—Original Design

In practice three main objections to this machine are (i) the difficulty of maintaining the rotary valve tight against vacuum, (ii) the insufficient working of the wetted clay, and (iii) the pockets do not always empty so that the feed of dry clay is not maintained constant. This design has been developed in this country and in America and the machines as at present used are as shown by Figs. 79 and 80.

The British development is shown by Fig. 79. The rotary valve has been retained but has been redesigned so that it will now hold against vacuum for very long periods of time. From the rotary valve the dry ground clay falls into a closed cylindrical mixer which is under vacuum. The central shaft has blades which mix the clay and propel it along the barrel under the water sprays where further mixing of the wetted clays takes place and towards the end of the barrel the clay is picked up by an auger and extruded through the die. The rate of clay feed, being controlled by the rotary valve, is constant and the rate of water fed to the sprays is indicated by a flowmeter.

The Americans have developed along rather different lines as shown on Fig. 80. The rotary valve has been dispensed with and the water is not added to the clay under vacuum. As in the British machine the clay is ground, screened, proportioned and mixed dry before feeding to the vacmixer. The feed is usually by belt conveyor feeder which feeds the clay into a vertical spray chamber, the clay first falling on to baffle plates to ensure that a thin curtain of clay particles falls down the centre of the spray chamber. The sprays are fitted in the sides of the chamber, below the baffle

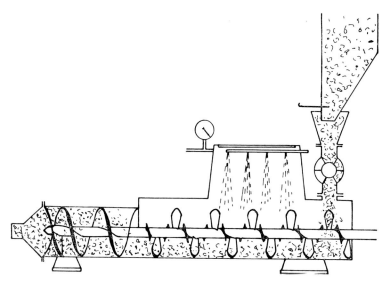

Fig. 79   Vac-mixer—British Development

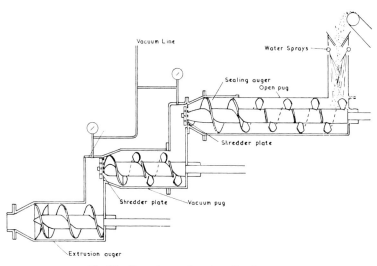

Fig. 80   Vac-mixer—American Development

plates, and the clay is wetted as it falls through the water spray. The wetted clay falls into an open trough mixer which terminates in a barrel and taper section fitted with a shredder plate at the end. In the open trough section the central shaft is fitted with knives but in the cylinder and taper section is a complete auger. The clay is extruded through the shredder plate, where it is cut by a shredder knife, into a de-airing chamber to a second barrel having a central shaft fitted with knives and a wing knife which extrudes through a shredder plate into a second de-airing chamber. In the centre chamber therefore the clay is mixed and pugged under vacuum. The clay extruded through the second shredder plate is cut by a shredding knife as it passes into the second de-airing chamber and is finally extruded by a normal auger and wing knife through the die. In this machine the water is not added to de-aired clay but the central sealed, and de-aired, pugging chamber ensures thorough mixing and break up of the clay under vacuum and, it is claimed, has proved very successful with difficult clays.

10 : Experiments in Extrusion

Experiments have been carried out to determine the laws of clay flow in extruders and to establish principles of design to obtain an efficient machine. These experiments show that a certain minimum pressure has to be developed in the mouthpiece before any extrusion at all can be obtained. This minimum pressure may be termed the 'yield pressure'. It varies for different clays, and for the same clay with different water contents. An analysis of the results shows that for any clay the 'yield pressure' varies exponentially with the water content according to the equation:

Yield pressure $= Ae^{-\alpha m}$

where A and α are constants for a particular clay but whose value varies for different clays.

Once the 'yield pressure' has been exceeded the rate of extrusion varies directly with the increase of pressure above the 'yield pressure' for all rates of extrusion, from very low rates up to the maximum possible. Results for a Staffordshire fireclay extruded from an auger having a mean helix angle of 15 degrees are given by Fig. 81. It will be noticed that, within the usual range of water contents, the 'yield pressure' and the maximum pressure both increase and the rate of extrusion falls off as the water content is reduced. It will also be seen, particularly at the lower water contents, that maximum rate of extrusion does not occur at maximum speed of rotation of the auger but that as the water content is reduced the auger speed necessary to give maximum rate of extrusion is reduced. This is probably seen better in Fig. 82 which shows the rate of extrusion plotted against auger speed for different water contents. At any water content the rate of extrusion increases with increase of auger speed up to an optimum value but once this optimum speed is exceeded the rate of extrusion begins to fall off

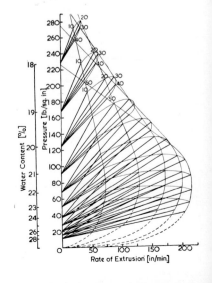

Fig. 81   Extrusion Tests—
Pressure/Rate of Extrusion

and zero rate of extrusion is obtained when the auger speed is approximately twice the speed that gives the maximum rate of extrusion.

The maximum possible theoretical value for rate of extrusion would be if the whole of the clay in the barrel moved along the auger as a nut on a screw. Then the rate of extrusion would be equal to the volume of clay enclosed in one turn of the helix multiplied by the number of revolutions. Since the volume of one turn of the helix is constant, the maximum possible theoretical rate of extrusion is proportional to the speed of rotation. This is indicated by the straight line on Fig. 82.

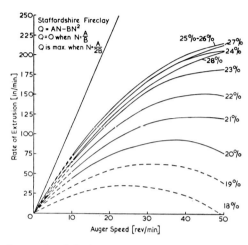

Fig. 82 Extrusion Tests—
Rate of Extrusion/Auger Speed

In practice the actual rate of extrusion falls far short of this theoretical maximum and this can be explained as follows.

If we assume no resistance to clay flow, that is to say the machine is working without spacer and die, then at very low speeds, which correspond to low rates of shear, the clay will be dragged along the barrel by the rotating screw with plug flow and, if the helix of the screw is kept full, the rate of extrusion per revolution of the screw will be equal to the volume enclosed in one turn of the helix. In other words it would be equal to the theoretical maximum. As the auger speed is increased part of the clay would travel along the screw with plug flow and part with laminar flow so that the rate of extrusion is less than if it were wholly plug flow. As the speed is further increased a point is reached when all the clay moves with laminar flow and if the speed is increased to a very high speed the flow approaches nearer and nearer to viscous flow in which the maximum rate of extrusion is only half that which it would be if the clay moved with plug flow.

So far we have considered only extrusion against no resistance with all the clay dragged along the cylinder by the action of the rotating screw. This could not happen in a normal machine under working conditions because the whole object of the machine is to extrude the clay in a consolidated column through a die. This necessitates a pressure in the mouthpiece and this pressure acts in all directions. It not only forces the clay in the mouthpiece to be extruded through the die but it also forces some of the clay in helix of the screw back along the helix towards the feed box and so reduces the net amount dragged along by the screw. It also tends to force the clay in the clearance between the tips of the auger and the barrel back through the clearance to the feed box and this clay must be replaced by some of that being dragged forward by the screw. If therefore we represent the amount of clay dragged along by the rotating helix against no pressure by Q_D, the back-pressure flow within the helix by Q_P, and the leakage flow through the clearance by Q_L then the net flow through the die can be represented by:

$$Q = Q_D - Q_P - Q_L.$$

Experimental results suggest that the maximum rate of extrusion is given by the equation:

$$Q_{max} = AN - BN^2$$

This means that the maximum possible rate of extrusion increases with increase of speed from zero when $N=0$ to its optimum value when $N=\frac{A}{2B}$, after which it decreases with further increase of speed until it falls to zero again when $N=\frac{A}{B}$, or in other words, the rate of extrusion is zero when the speed of the auger is twice the speed that gives optimum rate of extrusion. Under such conditions the sum of the back pressure flow Q_P, and the leakage flow Q_L is equal to the drag flow, Q_D.

This explains why it is sometimes possible to increase the rate of extrusion by reducing the auger speed, although this can only be achieved if the original speed exceeded the optimum speed for that particular clay. For example it has been reported that one large extruder in the U.S.A. extruded 12,000 bricks per hour when running at 44 r.p.m. and consuming 360 h.p., but when the speed was reduced to 32 r.p.m. the output increased to 18,000 bricks per hour and the power consumption fell to less than 250 h.p.

Effect of Helix or Blade Angle: Experiments have shown that with a parallel extrusion barrel both maximum rate of extrusion and maximum efficiency of extrusion are obtained when the mean helix angle of the auger is about 23 degrees. They show no very great change within the range of 21 degrees to 25 degrees, but both fall off rapidly on either side of this range. This angle is obtained approximately, with a single-start auger, when the pitch, or lead, of the screw is equal to the outside diameter of the flights.

In the case of bladed pugs, optimum efficiency and optimum extrusion are obtained when the blades are set at an angle of 23 to 25 degrees to a plane at right angles to the axis of the shaft.

Efficiency of Extrusion: With any blade angle, or any mean helix angle, the efficiency of extrusion falls off with increase in speed. The efficiency of extrusion is the ratio of the clay h.p. to the shaft h.p. or if expressed as a percentage is 100 times this ratio.

The clay h.p. is the product of the rate of extrusion in cubic feet per minute and the pressure in lb. per square foot divided by 33,000.

The shaft h.p. is the product of the torque in lb. ft. and the speed in r.p.m. multiplied by $\frac{2\pi}{33,000}$.

It is difficult in a works extruder to measure either the clay h.p. or the shaft h.p. and so for a works investigation it is more convenient to use rate of extrusion per unit power. This is not the same as extrusion efficiency because it introduces both the electrical efficiency and the mechanical efficiency of the drive, neither of which is constant throughout the range of speed variation, so that if the rate of extrusion per unit power is plotted against shaft speed the curve obtained will not be identical to that obtained by plotting extrusion efficiency against speed. Both curves will however show that the rate of extrusion per unit power, and efficiency of extrusion, increase as the shaft speed is reduced.

72

From this it is apparent that to obtain best results the blade angle, or mean helix angle, should be about 23 degrees, which gives maximum rate of extrusion and maximum efficiency at any speed, and then to obtain the desired output by adjustment of speed.

Quality of Extruded Column: It is sometimes argued that a better column is extruded if a less efficient blade, or mean helix, angle is adopted. This ought not to be necessary if the clay is properly prepared. An auger extrusion machine is not a mixer—once the clay is trapped within the flight it cannot escape and there is no evidence of circulation within the helix. The clay is forced towards the die by the rotation of the screw but the pressure in the mouthpiece acts in the opposite direction tending to force the clay back again along the helix. The effect of this is to reduce the forward flow of the clay. The resistance to backward flow is however not uniform so the rate of retardation is not uniform across the whole cross-section of the helix. This is because the helix has constant pitch and consequently the helix angle varies, becoming less as the radius increases. This means that the clay has an easier path to travel nearer the hub and so the back-pressure flow is greatest nearest the hub. The forward flow to the die is therefore greatest at the periphery of the helix and minimum at the hub, so that differential flow takes place with attrition of the larger particles. It is because of this that the experimental results reported earlier in this chapter were not reproducible until the clay had been passed through the extruder a large number of times.

An inefficient auger therefore tends to reduce the size of the coarser particles by attrition, but this can be achieved better and more economically in the grinding and screening plant. It is therefore suggested that finer grinding and a smaller screen mesh to take out the larger particles would improve the body and allow a more efficient auger to be used. In the case of plastic preparation in a wet pan and smooth rolls, the final set of rolls should be differential high-speed rolls set close.

If a bladed pug is used, clay can slip between the blades and therefore a certain amount of mixing takes place as well as attrition of the clay due to differential flow. Any benefit that accrues from the use of an inefficient blade angle may be due to one, or both, of these causes. In either case the additional grinding and mixing can be done better in the preparation plant than in the extruder.

Some clays benefit from double pugging, the first pug extruding clots which are often stored in a humid atmosphere overnight, to allow time for the water to permeate between the individual clay particles thus improving the plasticity of the clay. The conditioned clots are then extruded in another machine. It is for this type of clay that German manufacturers use conditioning pits, or conditioning towers (Maukturms), which have been described in an earlier chapter.

Laminations: An inherent feature of all bladed, or screw, extruders is that the clay enters the mouthpiece in the form of a helical coil. As soon as the clay leaves the end of the auger helix, or wing knife, and the hub, there is a void in the clay which immediately before was occupied by metal. A film of water migrates to the surface carrying with it some of the very finest clay particles. At these surfaces there is now an excess of water and clay mineral, and in the spacer and die the helical coil has to be united by the pressure of the following clay behind it and the resistance of the die in front. This pressure forces the clay into the voids and if the nose of the hub is tapered, or radiused, to a point, the clay follows the contour of the nose, very closely. If the end of the auger or wing knife is not brought to a point, or to a small diameter, particularly if the spacer is too short, there may be a hollow core in the centre when the clay enters the die. In the die this core is flattened and owing to the rotation of the clay it shows in the extruded brick as an 'S' crack. To cure this, the nose of the auger, or wing knife, should be brought, as nearly as possible, to a point and the spacer lengthened.

Even, however, if this pronounced 'S' crack is eliminated there will still be a definite clay structure that may show up as laminations in the extruded column, although in many cases they are quite innocuous.

Freezing a thin cross-section of the extruded column will usually show this structure to be of spiral formation in the cross-section. These spirals are the traces of the cut surface produced by the auger or wing knife. Although freezing a section of the green column shows spiral laminations, this does not necessarily mean that the bricks are faulty, particularly if the clay has been de-aired. The freezing technique is a very severe test. However, if spiral laminations show up after firing, or after weathering, either in the stock yard or in service then the trouble can be ameliorated by increasing the length of the spacer. If on doing this the freezing pattern changes to one in which the laminations are close together, near to and parallel to the four faces of the die, then the die should be shortened.

A general rule in the design of mouthpieces is, the more plastic the clay the longer the spacer and the shorter the die, whereas the leaner the clay the shorter the spacer and the longer the die.

If modifications to the spacer and die do not effect a cure then it becomes necessary to modify the clay mix. The addition of some sand or coarse grog will usually effect an improvement in a very plastic clay because, during differential flow, the coarse grog tends to tear the traces of the cut formed by the helix so roughening the surfaces and helping them to join together. On the other hand there are a few clays which are too lean and do not contain sufficient clay mineral to form an effective join. These can be improved by adding a plasticizer or plastic clay.

Balancing the Die: We have noted that if the die is too long the resistance of the die causes the clay nearest to the metal of the die to be held back resulting in differential flow which causes slip planes to be formed near to and parallel to the faces of the die. This can usually be cured by more effective lubrication or by shortening the die. It sometimes happens that differential flow results from uneven velocity in the die due to other causes. For example it may be that one side of the die extrudes at a faster rate than the other. This may show up in the extruded column which, instead of coming out straight, is curved. If however the top runs faster than the bottom the column cannot bend downwards because it is prevented from doing so by the table. Also if the bottom runs faster than the top the weight of the extruded column is sufficient to prevent it from curling upwards. Again the four corners may not extrude as fast as other positions of the die. If the centre tends to extrude faster than the sides then, even though the brick is cut with two parallel flat faces on the wire-cutting table, on drying and firing the strains will be relieved and the leading face of the brick may be concave and the trailing face convex.

Balancing the die means getting the clay to extrude at as nearly a constant rate as possible over the whole surface of the die. Probably the best way of doing this is to cut the column, whilst it is being extruded, into 15 separate columns by means of 4 vertical and 2 horizontal wires stretched taut across the face of the die as shown in Fig. 83. If this indicates that the clay is being extruded faster at one side than the other, then the whole die should be moved over towards that side which is moving the faster. If the four corners lag behind the rest of the column, the corners should be opened out at the back, i.e. at the entrance face of the die, in order to ease the flow at the corners. Attention should also be paid to the lubrication of those parts of the die where the clay flow is slow. If after this the centre still travels faster, improvement is often obtained by lubrication of the spacer.

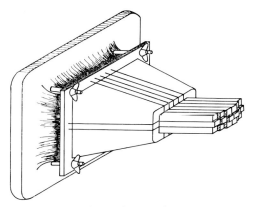

Fig. 83   Balancing of Die

Die Lubrication: The usual lubricants used for lubricating dies are water, steam and oil. The object of lubricating the die is to reduce the friction between the clay column and the metal walls of the die. It reduces the drag at the outside of the column and so reduces differential flow between various sections of the column. This is achieved by applying a thin film, of low shear strength, between the consolidated clay and the metal walls of the die. Water, oil, steam and air are all suitable for lubricating the die but owing to the pressure of clay in the mouthpiece it is essential to apply the lubricant under a pressure which is slightly higher than the pressure of the clay, otherwise it is unable to form a film. Air is a good lubricant but is seldom used since small leakages result in a much higher power consumption for lubrication. The choice between water, steam and oil generally depends upon the nature of the clay being extruded. Some clays extrude better with water, some with steam and some with oil. Sufficient lubricant must be applied but too much is not only unnecessary but also undesirable. Particular attention should be paid to the corners because here two sides of the column are in contact with metal.

Electrical lubrication of dies has been tried but is not very satisfactory. The principle of electrical lubrication is as follows. If a consolidated piece of clay is placed between two metal plates that are connected across an electric battery, then when the current is switched on, some of the water in the clay accumulates at the surface in contact with the plate of negative polarity (cathode) whilst the clay in contact with the plate of positive polarity (anode) becomes drier. This phenomenon is called electro-endosmosis. If therefore a metal rod is mounted centrally in the die, suitably insulated from the die and pug body, and if positive polarity is applied to the rod and negative polarity to the die, which is also earthed, a current will flow through the clay and water will be deposited at the surface of the die. The reason why it is unsatisfactory is threefold. First, the current always takes the shortest path so that the current density is greatest at the centre of the two longer sides which are nearest to the centre rod and least at the corners which are furthest away. The lubricating effect is therefore greatest at the centre of the two longer faces and least at the four corners. This is exactly opposite to what is required, because any normal die requires maximum lubrication at the corners. Secondly, because the clay at the anode becomes drier its resistance increases resulting in decreased current which reduces the lubricating effect. Also the dry clay at the centre, if allowed to build up sufficiently, would result in a core in the centre of the brick. Thirdly, unless very great precautions are taken there is always the risk of electric shock to operatives. For these reasons water, steam or oil are preferred. Where water or steam are satisfactory they should be used, but for some clays oil is essential. One of the drawbacks of oil lubrication is that it forms an impervious film on the faces of the bricks which retards drying.

Spacer and Die Design: In the study of the flow of clay through the extruder it was noted, under the heading 'quality of extruded column', that the clay moves along the barrel at a higher rate at the periphery of the helix and slowest near the hub. Since the end turns of the auger are full of consolidated clay this means that the rotational velocity of the clay increases towards the hub. The helical ribbon of clay entering the mouthpiece therefore has little or no rotation near the barrel but at the hub may be rotating at the same, or nearly the same, rate of rotation as the auger. In order to extrude a good column as free from laminations as possible it is essential that this rotation should be arrested before the clay enters the die.

Since the rotation is greatest at the centre and there is little or no rotation at the outside there is little to be gained by cutting flutes in the surface of the spacer, except that it prevents the outer layers of clay from being dragged round by the clay in the centre, and this is generally achieved by changing the shape of the spacer from round, where it joins the barrel, to rectangular at the die end. The rotation of the clay is therefore arrested by the internal friction of the clay and since in a very plastic clay the internal friction is low the spacer must be comparatively long. With a lean clay the internal friction is high and a comparatively short spacer will suffice.

Hence the rule that the more plastic the clay the longer the spacer and the leaner the clay the shorter the spacer.

The die itself produces the finished shape and because a plastic clay can be shaped easier than a lean clay the length of the die should be short for a plastic clay and long for a lean clay. In fact for some very plastic clays a plate die is often sufficient. By this is meant, that instead of a die, a steel plate about 1 inch thick, having a rectangular hole of the size of the column to be extruded, is bolted directly on to the end of the spacer. Plate dies are usually chamfered or radiused at the inlet edge leaving about $\frac{1}{2}$ inch of parallel die at the outlet end. Such dies are not lubricated.

The majority of clays are not excessively plastic nor excessively lean so that moderate lengths of spacer and die are usually used. It is however often worth while to experiment with the lengths of spacers and dies to see if any improvement can be achieved.

The taper of the die is important but there should always be a short parallel length of $\frac{1}{2}$ inch to about 1 inch at the exit end. The more plastic the clay the smaller the taper necessary and for plastic clays a taper of 8 degrees to 10 degrees half-angle upon the depth of the column and 4 degrees to 5 degrees half-angle upon the width is sufficient. For lean clays a steeper taper is necessary in order to develop more lateral pressure to shape the brick.

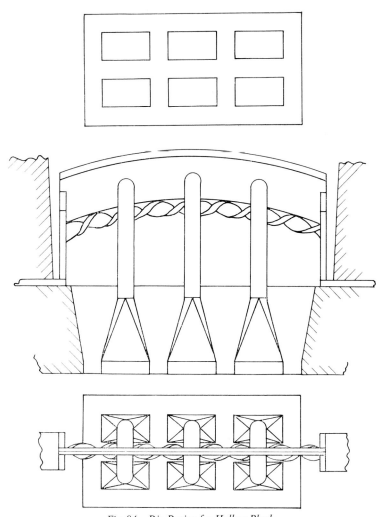

Fig. 84   Die Design for Hollow Block

For the extrusion of hollow blocks or perforated bricks the spacer should be of the same taper as for solid bricks. The dies however have to be fitted with cores which are attached to tines welded to a bridge or bridges. Owing to the reduction of cross sectional area and the increase of surface area due to the cores the resistance of the die is increased. In order to reduce this it is necessary to shorten the length of the die by an amount depending upon the increase in resistance to flow. If the area of the voids is large and the

77

clay wall thickness of the blocks or bricks is small it may be impossible to reduce the length sufficiently to bring down the resistance to that for a solid brick. In that case it will be necessary to extrude the clay at a softer consistency and/or extrude at a slower rate.

The bridge cuts the clay and if the bridge is smooth the clay may have difficulty in rejoining, so to assist the knitting together of the clay it is necessary to roughen the trailing edge of the bridge. One method of doing this, which has been found to be very satisfactory, is to twist a piece of flat bar and weld it to the trailing edge of the bridge. This tears the clay as it leaves the bridge leaving roughened surfaces which knit together better. The leading edge of the bridge may be ground to a chisel edge. A typical core arrangement is shown by Fig. 84.

The positioning of the cores is important. The core assembly is usually mounted on the back of the die and the bridge should extend into the spacer so that the leading edge of the bridge is as close as possible to the end of the auger, provided there is sufficient space between them to allow the clay to consolidate, so that the bridge cuts a solid column of clay. This distance is usually 4 inch to 6 inch. The cores themselves are mounted on the end of tines and are tapered with a short parallel length at the end, usually $\frac{1}{4}$ to $\frac{1}{2}$ inch length, of the correct dimensions. The ends of the cores should usually be exactly in line with the end of the die.

The core tips may be of heat-treated abrasion-resisting cast iron, tool steel or tungsten carbide. Generally cast iron cores are used unless the material is exceptionally abrasive.

De-airing: The majority of wire-cut bricks are extruded from de-airing machines because de-airing the clay results in a more plastic column which is tougher and, because the air has been removed, the cut surfaces produced by the auger and wing knife join together more effectively. Laminations due to cutting by the auger are therefore generally less serious, although they are not eliminated.

To obtain the best de-aired column it is essential to use the correct vacuum. This varies from clay to clay being higher for lean clays than for plastic clays. The best vacuum to use is the minimum necessary to extrude clay of maximum density. If insufficient evacuation is applied faults in the column are sometimes accentuated and the resulting column is not so good as if extruded without de-airing at all.

A method, suggested by a German manufacturer, for establishing the best vacuum for a particular clay is to extrude first with no evacuation at all. If the bricks are cut singly, carefully weigh three consecutive bricks. If a multi-wire cutter is used, extrude three columns and weigh one brick from each column cut by the same wires. The three bricks should be of the same weight but if there is much variation repeat until three consecutive bricks are approximately the same weight. Note the mean weight and then repeat the test with a vacuum of 50 per cent, say 15 inch Hg. Repeat the tests increasing evacuation for each test by 10 per cent, or 3 inch Hg, and note the mean weight of the three bricks in each test. It will be found that the weight of the bricks will increase with increase in evacuation up to some optimum value. Any further increase in evacuation does not increase the weight and with some clays may even tend to reduce it. The correct vacuum to use is that which just gives bricks of maximum density, i.e. maximum weight. With plastic clays the correct vacuum may not exceed 85 per cent but for lean clays may be 95 per cent of total vacuum. It is always better to check the vacuum against the barometer reading because if the barometer reading is 28 inch then 95 per cent of total vacuum is 26·6 inch but if the barometer reading is 30 inch then 95 per cent of total vacuum is 28·5 inch Hg.

11 : Wire-cut Ancillaries

Cutting Table: The extruded clay column is cut into lengths by the cutting table to produce bricks of the desired size after firing. Thus the cutting table is the final machine in the manufacturing line for bricks made by the wire-cut process.

Cutting tables are of five general types.
1. Hand driven, side cutting tables.
2. Hand operated, power driven, side cutting tables.
3. Automatic side cutting tables.
4. Automatic reel cutting tables.
5. Chopping-type cutting tables.

In each of these the height of the table is adjusted to be exactly in line with the bottom edge of the extruded column as it leaves the die. In order that the clay column will slide easily over the table it is usually passed over one or more rollers which run in an oil bath to lubricate the underside of the column. The table itself, which is usually covered with brass or zinc, is also kept lubricated by a film of oil.

With a hand driven, side cutting table the extruded column passes over lubricated rollers at the end of the table and when sufficient length for the required number of bricks has passed the single cutting wire, it is cut off by pulling the lever to draw the wire through the column. The piece cut off is pushed, by hand, along the table into position in front of the pressure board. The other lever is then pulled and the column of clay is pushed through the cutting wires by the pressure board.

The hand operated, power driven, side cutting table shown by Fig. 85 is similar to the hand power table except that the pressure board is power operated. The mechanism is provided with an automatic throw-out gear which comes into operation after completion of the cut.

Fig. 85   Hand Operated, Power Driven, Cutting Table

For larger outputs a double-sided power driven cutting off table, Fig. 86, may be used. In this machine the cut bricks are delivered alternately to one side and then to the other thus allowing more time for the removal of the cut bricks.

Fig. 86   Double Cutting-off Table

The main disadvantage of these machines is that the column cut is of varying lengths and the cut is not square, so two scrap ends have to be produced for each column cut. These scrap ends are contaminated with oil and so should not be returned direct to the feed box of the extruder, because the oil prevents the clay from adhering to other clay and so may tend to cause lamination cracks. The scrap ends should be returned to the preparation machines.

To avoid cutting with waste ends a travelling table is used. This type of table is mounted on runners which allow it to move in the direction of extrusion and the bricks are cut whilst the clay column is moving with the table.

In one form of hand operated table, Fig. 87, the column issuing from the die passes over the table and when of the correct length it pushes against a

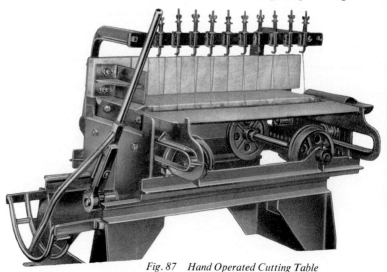

Fig. 87   Hand Operated Cutting Table

vertical stop which pushes the table forward. A single cutting wire then cuts the column squarely to the exact length to form the number of bricks to be cut. The table, bearing the column cut off to the correct length, is pulled further forward clear of the advancing column and then, actuated by a handle, the back board pushes the column through the cutting wires and the bricks are pushed on to boards, or pallets. The table is then pushed back and the operations are repeated.

Fully automatic cutting tables are similar to the power operated cutting tables except that the clay column operates a trip to set the cutting operation in motion. A cutting table of this type is shown by Fig. 88. In the hydraulically-operated cutting table, Fig. 89, when the column reaches the stop, it not only moves the table forward, but also operates the hydraulic

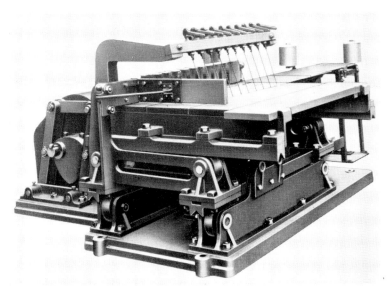

Fig. 88   Automatic Cutting Table

Fig. 89   Hydraulically Operated Cutting Table

control valve and the cutting is done by a hydraulically-operated piston. A pneumatically-operating cutting table is shown by Fig. 90. In this machine the clay column passes over a measuring belt which operates a valve controlling a pneumatic piston coupled to a single cutting wire. This cuts the column to exact length. The cut column then accelerates on a conveyor belt which brings it up against a stop which operates another valve controlling the cutting mechanism.

Fig. 90   Pneumatically Operated Cutting Table

Automatic, power operated reel cutters are used for high outputs and for stiff extrusion and so are becoming more popular. A hand operated reel cutter is shown by Fig. 91 and an automatic reel cutter by Fig. 92.

Fig. 91   Hand Operated Reel Cutter

Fig. 92   Automatic Reel Cutter

The Frey automatic cutter Fig. 93 may be fitted with one, two or three cutting wires. Its maximum speed of operation is 1 cut per second so that with a single wire it will cut up to 3,600 bricks per hour, with two wires up to 7,200 and with three wires up to 10,800 bricks per hour. The wires are horizontal and cut downwards. The length of cut is set by chain wheels and the extruded column passes over a woven felt measuring belt which at one end passes over an expanding measuring roller. By adjustment of this measuring roller the length of cut can be adjusted to within 0·5 per cent of the desired length. The movement of the measuring belt by the clay column operates the cutting mechanism through a torque amplifier which supplies additional frictional energy through a belt-driven pulley from a counter-shaft or electric motor.

Fig. 93   Frey Automatic Cutter

Another automatic cutting table is the Keller machine, Fig. 94. This machine has a single cutting wire which chops the bricks singly from the

83

Fig. 94   Keller Automatic Cutter

extruded column. In this machine also the clay passes over a measuring belt which operates the cutting mechanism through a torque amplifier, power being supplied by a separate motor.

The Frey and Keller cutting machines are more suitable for cutting columns of a fairly soft consistency.

Sand-faced Wire-cut Bricks: In many districts sand-faced bricks are popular. They are made by extrusion, in which case the column is sand-blasted before cutting, or by the stiff-plastic process when the green pressed bricks pass through the sand-blast machine on a conveyor. A typical sand-blast machine for this purpose is shown by Fig. 95 and comprises a mild steel cabinet totally enclosed except for an opening at each end through which the bricks are fed on a belt conveyor. A sand hopper feeds the sand to two oscillating nozzles inside the cabinet and by compressed air, or steam, the sand is blown onto the bricks, completely and evenly sanding them on one stretcher and two headers. By the use of different grades of sand and by adjusting the air, or steam pressure, any desired penetration can be obtained. A separate exhaust fan is supplied to extract dust, or alternatively a combined dust extractor and collector may be used but the latter is not recommended when steam is used. The machine is driven by a 1 h.p. motor and a further 2 h.p. is required for the separate exhaust fan or dust extractor and collector. The output can be regulated from 1,000 to 10,000 bricks per hour.

Fig. 95   Sand-blast Machine

Rustic Bricks: Rustic bricks have a rough, pleasing appearance and the roughening of the surface can be produced in many ways.

One of the simplest ways is to cut a thin slice from the top and two sides of the column being extruded, by wires a short distance in front of the die. The wires may be mounted on a frame in such a manner that the tension on the wires can be adjusted. The wire should not be too thin or too taut or the surface will be too smooth. At the same time it should not be too slack. With the correct diameter of wire and the correct tension very pleasing surfaces can be obtained on many clays. The depth of the cut will vary for different clays. For some it is sufficient just to scrape the surface whilst for others it may be necessary to cut off a slice ¼ inch or more in thickness.

Some clays give a better surface with a thicker wire than others and some prefer a brass wire. The object of the wires is not so much to cut the clay as to tear it and for some clays it may be desirable to mount the wires on springs as this allows a certain amount of vibration which produces a rougher surface.

The slices cut from the sides fall away but the slice cut from the top should be diverted to fall to one side of the column. This is best done by mounting a thin sheet of metal, just clear of the surface of the column, about 1 inch in front of the wire. The slice of clay feeds onto this sheet and a deflector can be arranged on it to divert the clay slice to one side or the other.

Sometimes a steel or brass bar filed to a blunt chisel edge is more satisfactory than a wire, and sometimes a sheet of metal is better. With either of these some experiments should be carried out to find the best angle of inclination (usually between 10 degrees and 30 degrees) and the best depth of cut to produce the desired result.

Dabbing with a wire brush produces a stippling effect and machines are available to do this mechanically. One such machine is illustrated by Fig. 96 which rusticates the two headers and one stretcher face at one operation.

Fig. 96   Rusticating Machine

The machine can be placed between the extrusion die and the cutting off table so that the column is cut after rustication or it may be used as an independent machine in which the cut bricks are rusticated. In some cases, when the material is very soft, it is better to do the rustication after partial drying when the bricks are suitably firm for handling. The machine may also be used for rusticating stiff-plastic bricks. It is fitted with a variable speed drive so that the output of the machine can be adjusted as required. Three cutter heads are fitted to the machine each being fitted with high-carbon steel cutters, each cut irregularly to effect the staggering of the impressions on the bricks, and apart from the 'dabbing' action the cutter heads partially rotate through an angle of 3 degrees. The machine is transportable and is driven by a 1 h.p. motor supplied with electricity by a flexible lead.

Re-pressing Wire-cut Bricks: Wire-cut bricks are often re-pressed to obtain a better surface finish with sharp corners. Sometimes, however, it is done to imprint a pattern on the faces of the bricks—the pattern of bark used to be quite popular—but in this case a collapsible mould is essential.

At one time, when extrusion was carried out with softer clay than is now usual, the bricks, after cutting, were allowed to stand for a time to stiffen before re-pressing. To avoid the cost of double handling it is now usual to extrude at a sufficient stiffness to allow re-pressing immediately.

Hand-operated presses are still used at some works but the majority of presses are now of the semi-automatic, power driven type. These are supplied by most of the manufacturers of clay-working machinery and a typical semi-automatic, power driven, screw press is shown by Fig. 97. The brick is placed in the mould and the operating lever depressed which causes the friction wheel on the screw to rotate so forcing the top die into the mould. Releasing the operating lever reverses the rotation of the screw and lifts the top die out of the mould. By depressing the lever twice two pressures can be given to the brick in the mould. The brick is lifted out of the mould by means of a pedal. In the latest designs of this type of press an interlocking guard is fitted so that the top die cannot be driven downwards, even if the operating handle is depressed, unless the guard has been put into the safe position.

86

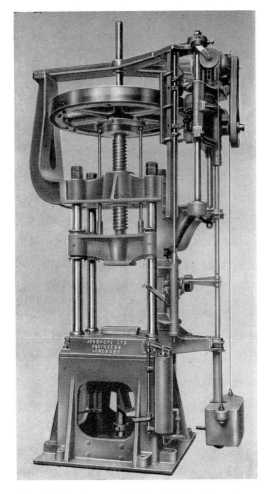

Fig. 97   Semi-automatic, Power Driven, Screw Press

Another type of press used for re-pressing is the eccentric-operated press, an example of which is shown by Fig. 98. Some of these are fitted with a clutch which stops the press after one revolution.

The 'Derby' press, Fig. 99, is an eccentric-operated press with automatic feed and discharge specially designed for the re-pressing of wire-cut bricks. If the bricks are sanded before re-pressing, a collapsible mould is used, in which event the bricks are fed to the mould, and taken off, by hand.

For re-pressing wire-cut bricks heavy pressures are not required and so toggle presses, which are generally used for high pressures, are not generally used. The more plastic the clay the lower the pressure necessary, so that for any particular clay the higher the water content the lower the pressure required, and conversely the lower the water content the higher the pressure required.

Fig. 98   Eccentric Operated Press

Fig. 99   Derby Press

12 : Semi-dry Pressing

Bricks made by the semi-dry process usually have about 6 to 8 per cent of water as made, although some clays require much higher moisture contents. For example Fletton bricks are made by semi-dry pressing from clay containing about 20 per cent moisture. The clay is prepared by dry grinding, generally in a dry pan in which the necessary amount of water is added, screening and storing the ground clay in large quantities in a dust loft or storage silo to allow the water to penetrate the clay grains, and finally by pressing in a press.

Because the clays used for making bricks by the semi-dry process contain less water than is required for any other process, the forming pressure required to produce good bricks is maximum. Consequently strongly built presses are necessary.

Three main types of mechanical presses are used for semi-dry pressing. They are:

1. Crank or eccentric operated.
2. Cam operated.
3. Toggle operated.

In all cases they are fitted with automatic feed boxes which are connected by means of a tube to the dust loft, or to a storage hopper, as the case may be, above the press.

The usual type of press used in this country for making building bricks by the semi-dry process is illustrated by Fig. 100. The mould box is fitted

Fig. 100   Semi-dry Press

into the press table so that the top of the mould is flush with the top of the table. The bottom die plate is operated by a cam underneath, and the top die, which may be heated by steam or electricity, is mounted on a crosshead which slides in guides in the side frames and is operated by means of a crank and connecting rod on each side. The feed box is operated by means of levers from the large cams in the main wheels at the sides of the machine, the feed box being at the back of the machine.

The operation is as follows. The mould is filled with clay dust and the top die is pulled down by the connecting rods and cranks. When this is in its lowest position the bottom die plate is given two impact pressures by a cam and then the top and bottom dies are raised together, thus lifting the brick out of the mould. The bottom die stops when it is flush with the table but the top die continues to rise clear of the brick. The feed box now moves forward, pushing the pressed brick clear of the mould, the bottom die descends and the clay dust in the feed box falls into the mould. The feed box is then retracted, the front plate scraping the clay dust level with the top of the mould. The top die then descends and the whole operation is repeated. The volume of clay in the mould is controlled by means of a handwheel which raises or lowers the position of the bottom die plate. The operation of the machine is entirely automatic, except for adjustment of the amount of clay in the feed box. The bricks are pressed two at a time and the output is approximately 1,200 bricks per hour.

One press of this type is fitted with an automatic feed control[1] which

Fig. 101   Semi-dry Press—Automatic feed adjustment

Ref. 1. Clayton Goodfellow. Brit. Pat. 665,281.

works as follows. On top of the connecting rod above the crosshead centre is a series of flat springs working in an oil bath. These are tempered and accurately ground to give a constant deflection at a definite load. This deflection operates, through electrical switch gear, a small fractional-h.p. reversing motor which is coupled to the feed-regulating shaft so that if an underload is registered the motor turns the shaft until sufficient feed has been added and if an overload is registered the motor turns the shaft in the opposite direction until the load becomes normal. The normal load gives a range of 3 tons between an underload and an overload. Most of the time the press will be working within these limits and the mechanism is then not operating. A gauge on the top of the mechanism indicates the pressure being exerted by the machine, and is useful in determining the pressure necessary to produce the required quality of bricks, and is also used when adjusting the measuring device to produce this result. Fig. 101 shows the motor coupled to the feed-regulating shaft and also shows the oil level indicator on the cover of the leaf spring box with the pressure gauge on top.

Some semi-dry presses of this type not only press the bricks but also re-press them to obtain greater consolidation and a better surface finish. The operation of the press is shown diagrammatically by Fig. 102. The clay is

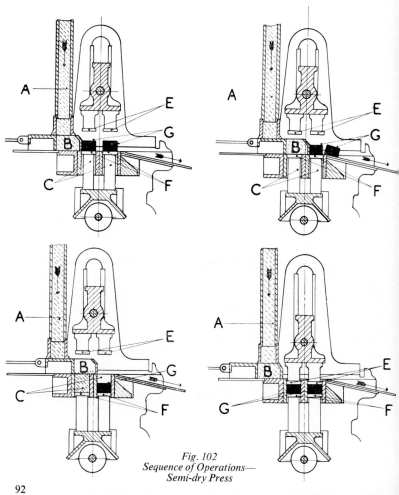

Fig. 102
Sequence of Operations—
Semi-dry Press

fed through pipe A into the feed box B which moves forward pushing the pressed brick from the first mould to the second. The bottom plungers descend, the clay from the feed box fills the mould and the pressed brick is lowered into the second mould. The feed box is retracted and the top dies descend, pressing the ground clay in the first mould into a brick and re-pressing the brick in the second mould. Whilst the top dies are in their lowest position two pressures are applied by the bottom dies in quick succession and then the dies are raised, to the position shown by the first diagram, ejecting the bricks. The sequence of operations is then repeated.

The Stanley semi-dry press is a cam-operated machine. The mould is filled by means of a reciprocating feed-box, similar to that already described, but pressure is applied from the top only by means of specially shaped cams and rollers. The pressure is at first applied slowly and then slightly relieved, to allow escape of air, and finally applied fully by pressure of the cam.

The Platt machine is also cam operated but in this case the cam lifts the crosshead carrying the top die. In operation, the crosshead and die fall on to the material in the mould twice in a complete cycle thus forming the brick by impact pressure.

The Spengler press is a German machine which is cam operated. It is a rotary table press and the sequence of operations which is as follows is depicted by Fig. 103. The intermittently rotating table first passes the moulds beneath the filling mechanism and then to the first preliminary pressing station where pressure is applied from the top only by the falling of the upper piston under its own weight. The piston is then raised slightly, effecting de-airing on the upper face. The brick is then given a second preliminary pressing from above and below after which the lower piston descends slightly effecting de-airing on the bottom face. The brick is then given its final pressing from above and below at maximum pressure. The upper piston then withdraws from the mould and the lower piston rises to the level of the top of the mould so ejecting the brick. The brick is moved to the discharge slide whence it is withdrawn and the bottom die descends to its initial filling position for the next cycle. The output of this press is said to be 2,000 bricks per hour. Hydraulic pressure compensation is fitted to prevent excessive pressures if the mould is too full.

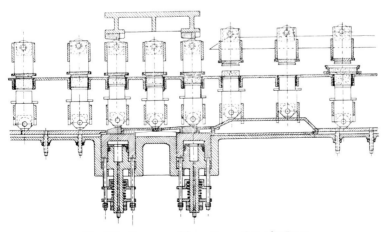

Fig. 103   Sequence of Operations—Spengler Press

The 'Hercules' press made by H. Alexander & Co. Ltd., is another rotary table press. The table is rotated intermittently by means of a ratchet gear operated from the crankshaft and pressure is applied from the bottom die which is actuated by means of a heavy cast steel beam from the crankshaft. The pressure is applied against a steel anvil immediately over the top of the mould. The feed pan is a circular container which sits on the top of the rotating table and steel stirrers prevent segregation of the materials. The presses are made in various sizes: The 'Eight' has a theoretical output of 1,200 bricks per hour and is driven by a 10 h.p. motor, and the 'Twelve' has a theoretical output of 1,800 bricks per hour and is driven by a 15 h.p. motor.

The Sutcliffe Speakman 'Emperor' press is also a rotary table press but in this machine the brick gets two pressings by the same ram. In the latest designs the pressure is applied through two tapered plates, one fixed but adjustable, the other sliding and operated by a pneumatic cylinder, the valves being controlled by a cam. The first pressure is applied with the sliding plate withdrawn, the pressure is then released and the sliding taper plate is pushed forward to reduce the clearance and the pressure is again applied by the same plunger. Because of the introduction of the taper plate the second pressure compacts the brick more than the first and during the relief of pressure between the two pressings air is allowed to escape. In this press also the pressure is applied from below against an anvil on the top of the mould.

The American 'Boyd' press, Fig. 104, is a toggle lever press in which pressure is exerted upon both top and bottom faces of the brick in the mould.

Fig. 104   Boyd Press

A special feature of this press is the automatic de-airing pause at a selected point in the compression stroke. This pause, the length of which can be regulated, is said to allow air to escape from the partially compressed material and allows time for the orientation of grains in the mix. A pause of one second is usually sufficient. After the pause the compression stroke is automatically completed. The press is made in two sizes, each working at a speed of 8 strokes per minute. At this speed the smaller model, fitted with four moulds, has an output of 1920 standard (9 inch by $4\frac{1}{2}$ inch) bricks per hour and exerts a total pressure of 400 tons whilst the larger model, fitted with six moulds, has an output of 2,880 standard bricks per hour and exerts a total pressure of 600 tons.

Another similar American press is the 'International' but this is also fitted with an electronic device to control the amount of dust fed to the mould in order to ensure constant pressure so controlling the density of the pressed brick.

The 'President' press, Fig. 105, made by William Johnson & Son (Leeds) Ltd., instead of having a de-airing pause in a single compression stroke gives two pressures on both top and bottom faces of the brick in the mould, both pressures being live. The pressure can be regulated and between the two pressures is a de-airing pause which is not adjustable. Two sizes of press are made, the smaller exerting a total pressure of 180 to 200 tons and the larger a total pressure of 450 to 500 tons. Either press can be fitted with one, two or three moulds, but more moulds are not recommended owing to the difficulty of filling them all uniformly. The speed of operation is 8 strokes per minute so that the output with three moulds is 1,440 bricks per hour.

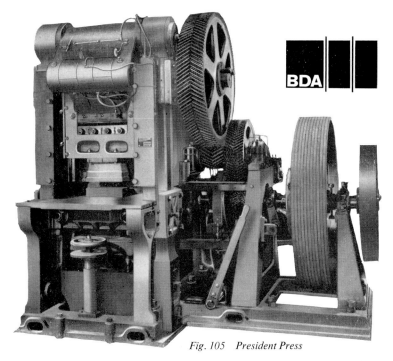

Fig. 105   President Press

The German 'Wormatia SKP' toggle lever press made by Friedrich Horn, of Worms am Rhein, gives a single compression stroke with no de-airing pause. It gives a total pressure of 300 tons and if fitted with three moulds has an output of 1,200 bricks per hour.

Causes of Cracks in Semi-dry Pressed Bricks: When loose particles of ground clay are fed into a mould, between 40 per cent and 50 per cent of the volume occupied is voids. These voids are full of air and if on compression some of this air is unable to escape before the sides and faces become sealed then the air is entrapped in the body of the brick and becomes compressed owing to the pressure applied. The brick may therefore contain one or more pockets of compressed air which, when the brick is released from the mould, tend to disrupt the brick. It is therefore essential that time should be allowed during pressing for the air to escape from the clay in the mould.

Sometimes the moulds and dies are de-aired. This is done by drilling very fine holes, or by making very fine slots of about 0·002 inch width in the mould liners or die plates and applying a vacuum. Great care must be taken to see that these small holes or fine slots do not get blinded by small particles of clay.

Cracking may also occur due to pressing at too high a pressure.

When the powder has been compacted in the mould there is a sideways pressure on the walls of the mould. This side pressure can be considered as the sum of two components, one is an elastic component due to the elasticity of the material and the other a plastic component due to the flow properties. When the ram pressure is released the elastic component disappears but the plastic component remains. The walls of the mould exert a pressure on the compact, by reaction, of the same amount and so hold the compact firmly in the mould. If on removal of the ram this component is excessive the residual stress may be sufficiently high to cause cracks to be formed when the brick is ejected, as shown by the dotted lines in Fig. 106, which may penetrate only a short distance from the walls sufficient to relieve the internal stress. The appearance of laminar fractures along the sides of the brick as it leaves the mould can be explained as follows. The first cracks appear when the ram is released by the stress concentrations mentioned above. As the brick emerges from the mould the stress concentrations move down the brick towards the end which is the last to leave and in doing so produce a series of cracks which produce a relief of stress. Because of these high residual pressures which remain in the brick after pressing the applied pressure should not be greater than that required to produce a good brick. Any excess of pressure may lead to cracking on release from the mould.

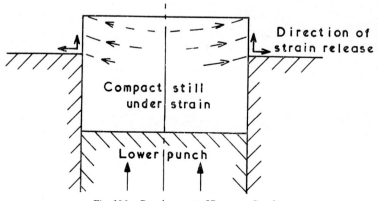

Fig. 106   Development of Pressure Cracks

13 : Stiff-plastic Process

The stiff-plastic process of making bricks appears to be indigenous to this country. The process is a combination of extrusion and pressing and is suitable for moderately hard clays and shales. The water content of the prepared clay is usually about 9 to 15 per cent which is higher than for semi-dry pressing but lower than for extruded bricks used in the wire-cut process of brickmaking.

The clays or shales are ground dry, usually in a dry pan, and screened. In most cases it is necessary to use a primary crusher to crush the pieces to 2 to 3 inch before feeding to the dry pan. After grinding and screening the clay is stored, usually on the dust loft floor but preferably in a hopper or silo. The feed to the brickmaking machine should be continuous and is usually controlled by a rotary disc feeder which feeds into a single- or double-shaft mixer in which the additional water necessary is added. The water should be added in the form of a fine spray through spray nozzles over as large an area of clay as possible as far back in the mixer as possible. By this means the water is added as uniformly as possible. If the water is added through a perforated pipe or an open-ended pipe some of the clay receives an excess of water and rolls up into balls with wet clay on the inside and collects drier clay on the outside so that the water distribution is by no means uniform. Very often two mixers are used, the first discharging into the second, but there is usually no resting period to allow the water to penetrate between the individual clay grains. Double-shafted mixers are better than single-shaft mixers which are little more than conveyors.

From the mixer the clay is fed into the brickmaking machine of which there are several different types. The principle of operation is to extrude the clay from a pug into a clot mould to form a clot of roughly the shape of the brick. The clot is then pressed in a mould to shape the brick and is often re-pressed.

In one type of machine, Fig. 107, the mixer feeds into a vertical pug which extrudes the clay directly into a mould in the intermittently rotating horizontal table. Each movement of the table brings an empty mould under

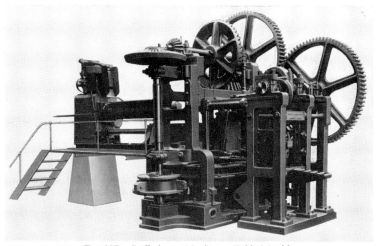

Fig. 107   Stiff-plastic Machine—Table Moulds

97

the pug mouthpiece and the table remains stationary while the mould is filled. The clots are carried round the table in their moulds to the position at which a clot is pushed out of the mould by the lifting of the bottom die. Whilst the table is stationary, the clot is raised to the level of the table, and is pushed off and delivered to the press by a self-operating linkage. As the table moves round to the next position the press head descends and presses the brick to shape. Each time the table comes to rest the empty clot mould under the pug is filled whilst, at the discharge position, the clot, raised to table level, is pushed under the press and pushes the already pressed brick on to the delivery table where it is usually picked off by hand and stacked on a stillage for transfer to the kiln. After the clot has been removed from the mould, during the next movement of the table the bottom die is lowered to its normal position and the inside of the mould is lubricated by spraying a fine mist of oil into it. Such a machine has an output of 1,200 bricks per hour but a larger machine with double clot moulds has an output of 2,000 bricks per hour.

By feeding the pressed bricks automatically into a second press, or re-press, a better finish is provided and stronger corners. The repress machine, Fig. 108, is usually used for facing-bricks and the single-press machine for commons.

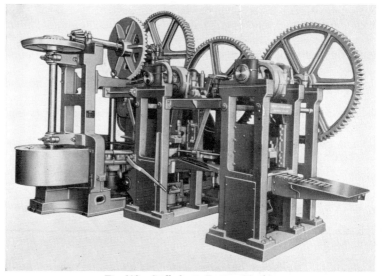

Fig. 108   Stiff-plastic Repress Machine

Another way of forming the clots is to extrude the clay into moulds cut in the periphery of a revolving drum as shown by Fig. 109. After forming the clot, the drum rotates to bring the next mould into position for filling. When the clot reaches the top of the drum it is pushed out sideways and fed

Fig. 109   Stiff-plastic Machine—Drum Moulds

under the press. A machine which has two intermittently rotating clot-mould drums is the Hewitt machine shown by Fig. 110. The vertical pug extrudes first into a mould in one drum and then into a mould in the other

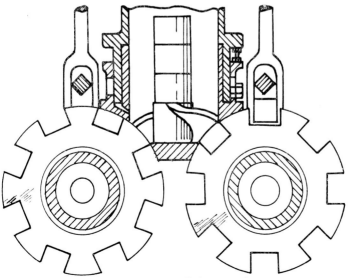

Fig. 110   Hewitt Stiff-plastic Machine

drum. The clots are pushed out of the moulds to one of two presses, each press being fed from its own drum. Extrusion and pressing take place alternately first one side and then the other. By this means the power necessary to drive the machine is reduced to little more than that required for a single machine and the output is claimed to be 2,500 bricks per hour.

A third method of forming the clots is to extrude alternately into two clot moulds 'A' mounted on a reciprocating table 'C'. The table is reciprocated by suitable linkage operated by double face cams 'D', shown by Fig. 111, or by a crankshaft which rotates through 180 degrees intermittently by a Geneva motion. The clots are ejected from the moulds by the push rods 'L' operated by the lever 'K' by means of the cam 'H'. The ejected clots are automatically pushed to one of two presses. Thus the clot moulds are filled alternately, and the bricks pressed alternately, so saving power. The output of such machines varies from 1,800 to 2,500 bricks per hour.

Fig. 111   Reciprocating Table Moulds

The presses used on stiff-plastic machines are of different designs but the pressure is usually applied by an eccentric. Sometimes toggle presses are used. In some machines equal pressures are applied above and below the clot but more generally the pressure is applied from the top only.

The press moulds are fitted with renewable steel liners and because the clot is only an approximate fit in the mould it is necessary to provide for the escape of air and excess clay from the mould. Air can escape round the top and bottom die and vent holes are provided usually in the bottom die plate to serve as a safety valve for the escape of clay if the clot is oversize.

Faults in Stiff-plastic Bricks: Faults in stiff-plastic bricks may be due to several causes. If the clot mould is not completely filled there will be insufficient clay in the clot to form a good brick. This usually shows up as a ragged or crumbly edge or corner, and generally indicates a worn auger or wing knife. A replacement will usually effect a cure.

If on the other hand the clot moulds are too large, then during pressing the pressure may be so high that high residual stresses are set up in those parts of the brick furthest away from the vent holes, whilst near the vent holes the stress has been relieved but planes of weakness may have been set

100

up due to differential flow caused by the extrusion of an excessive amount of clay through the vent holes. In such a case there will be unequal internal stresses in the brick which may not have any apparent effect on the brick until it is fired. It is therefore essential that the size of the clot should not be allowed to vary too much.

When a machine is fitted with a re-press the size of the clot is most important. It should be of such a size that the brick can be well shaped and of correct volume with the minimum of extrusion of clay through the vent holes. This will ensure that the brick is formed with the minimum pressure and the brick is then re-pressed at a higher pressure to obtain the desired finish and density. In the re-press mould there are no vent holes. As the clot moulds wear, the clots will get larger and more clay will be extruded through the vent holes but, if too much wear is allowed, cracking of the pressed bricks will occur.

Uneven distribution of clay in the clot mould will on pressing lead to variations in density in various parts of the brick which may also be a cause of trouble. Other causes, not so easily apparent, are due to insufficient preparation of the clay mix and particularly due to uneven water distribution.

14 : Production Quality Control

The necessity for controlling each operation in the manufacturing process has been emphasized earlier in this book. In the manufacture of bricks the first operation is the winning of the clay and it is here that the controls should commence.

Raw Material Control: The raw material available to the brickmaker varies from point to point of the working face and as the working face is advanced the nature of the clays may change so that the variations may also change. It is because of these variations that great care has to be exercised in winning, or large amounts of useless material may be fed to the preparation and making machines. Gross impurities such as large stones, large ironstone nodules, etc., can be picked out by hand, but smaller impurities will be included in the mix, unless an excess of these occurs at isolated points in the working face when those parts of the face can be discarded. Behind these pockets of impurities there may however be perfectly good clay.

It is because of these variations in the constitution of the clay face that it is necessary to determine the properties of the clay in advance of use, if production is to be kept under control. Since present tests take a day or so to complete and because the results of the tests should be available before the clay is fed to the preparation plant, samples representing the clays to be used in about a month's time should be sent regularly to the works laboratory.

When the clay is to go directly from the clay pit to the preparation plant, the only satisfactory method is to take samples by boring from those positions from which the clay will later be won.

If the clay, after winning, is weathered the samples may be taken from the weathering heap.

A blending heap, constructed as described on Pages 4–5, evens out the irregularities and ensures a more uniform mix. Thus with bulk blending there should be little variation in the samples taken from one blending heap, although samples from subsequent blending heaps may indicate a drift towards an excess, or deficit, of one particular seam. By taking samples from properly prepared blending heaps it is possible to determine whether more or less of any particular seam or stratum is to be included in the blending heap.

The object of taking the samples it to make tests to check whether the clay is suitable for the manufacture of good bricks, by the particular process in use at the works, and to see that the constitution of the clay does not drift out of control. From experience, aided by the results of the tests, it is possible to fix control limits beyond which the constitution of the clay mix must not be allowed to go.

The tests are simple physical tests, the results of which must be recorded for reference, and the tests must be made on an average standard mixture of the seams as used in the works for making the bricks. Suitable tests are:
1. The sample should be dry ground to pass 7 mesh, and inspected visually, preferably with a low-powered binocular microscope having a magnification of 20, to detect abnormal or undesirable material such as limestone, iron minerals, gypsum, etc.
2. Wet sieve analysis in which the amounts remaining on, and passing through, certain standard test sieves, e.g. 7, 36 and 72, from a known weight of sample are determined.
3. Moisture adsorption. Determining the percentage of water taken up by a sample of dried clay when stood for 24 hours over a saturated salt solution.
4. Sedimentation volume test. The apparent volume of 20 g of clay when allowed to settle in water.
5. Ignition loss.

These tests and their implications have been discussed very fully by P. S. Keeling in Chapter V of his book 'The Geology and Mineralogy of Brick Clays' in this series.

By means of the tests a check is kept on the constitution of the clay mix.
Grading Analysis: When clays are ground in a dry pan and screened it is advisable to keep a check on the grading analysis of the screened clay, particularly if it is to be used for making semi-dry-pressed bricks. The packing density will vary with the grading analysis so that the weight of material fed into the press mould will vary with the grading analysis. The grading analysis will also yield useful information about the effects of wear of the muller tyres, grinding plates and grids of the dry pan so that as well as ensuring constant packing density it also serves as a quality control check on the condition of the pan mill. For this test the clay should be sieved dry through standard screens, the former standard being 7, 16, 36 and 72 B.S.S., although sometimes the 36 mesh screen was omitted. It is now recommended that the Wentworth scale be used, the full range of screens being $\frac{3}{8}$ inch, $\frac{3}{16}$ inch, 7, 14, 25, 52, 100 and 200. If the test is to be used as a quality control check on the condition of the pan mill it is advisable that the feed to the pan mill should be continuous by means of an automatic feeder, otherwise variations in the rate of feed will result in variations in the grading analysis which may mask the effects of wear.

If the clay is fed into the pan with an automatic feeder at a constant rate, pre-crushed if necessary, then the effect of pan wear will be evident from the results and the maintenance staff can be instructed to carry out maintenance work before the grading analysis gets out of control.

For stiff-plastic making, and for extrusion when a dry pan is used, this test is not so satisfactory as the wet sieve analysis, already mentioned, as a control of the density of the finished bricks, but it would serve as a control of the condition of the pan mill.

Control of Water Content: It is well known to clay workers that there is some dependence between the pressure used in shaping a clay mix and its water content. For example, in hand moulding, in which low pressures are used, high moisture contents are necessary whilst for those methods of shaping involving high pressures, such as semi-dry or stiff-plastic pressing, relatively low moisture contents are used. The higher the pressure used the lower the moisture content needed to achieve the greatest density. There is, in fact, for a given making pressure an optimum moisture content above or below which products of less density will be produced. Furthermore research has shown that at the particular optimum pressure not only is the density of the product maximum but also its crushing strength is maximum

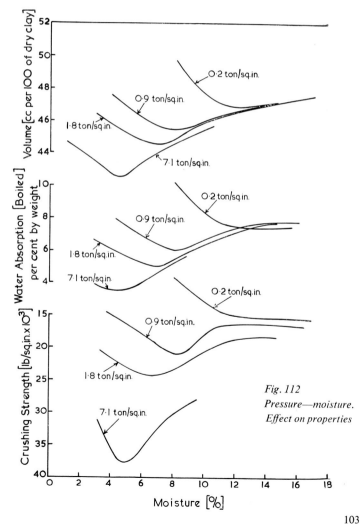

Fig. 112
Pressure—moisture.
Effect on properties

and water absorption minimum. The results of one series of tests on briquettes made from the same clay at different moisture contents and fired to the same temperature (1,100 degrees C.) are shown by Fig. 112. These curves are extremely interesting and clearly show an optimum moisture content for all methods of making because a pressure of 0.2 tons/square inch is about the pressure obtained in extrusion whilst semi-dry press methods are covered by the pressures of 1.8 and 7.1 tons/square inch. The 0.9 tons/ square inch represents the stiff-plastic region.

This investigation has brought into prominence the problem of controlling both water content and forming pressure for all methods of shaping. We have already noted the effect of variation in water content in the case of extruded columns on Page 70 but we now see that it is equally important for stiff-plastic and semi-dry press making.

The usual method of controlling the water additions to the clay mix at the present time is by manual control. The temperer judges from the appearance or feel of the clay whether more or less water is necessary and manipulates his control valve accordingly. This is not a very satisfactory method of control because his judgment may vary from day to day or even hour to hour and comparatively wide variations in water content occur throughout the day. It is therefore desirable that some form of automatic water control should be devised.

In the case of extrusion we have seen that there is a definite relationship between extrusion pressure and water content at a constant rate of extrusion. Water content is similarly related to torque. Thus we appear to have two methods of indicating variations in the amount of water in the mix supplied to an extruder.

The first method used to control the water content was by means of an ammeter, in circuit with the driving motor, placed in such a position that the temperer could see variations in consumption. If the ammeter reading increased it was assumed that the clay stiffness had increased and the temperer fed more water to the mix. If the ammeter reading fell below normal the clay was too soft and so the water addition was reduced. The ammeter reading was however found to be not sufficiently sensitive to moisture variations and the reading often varied for other reasons.

The next step was to fit strain gauges onto the mouthpiece. Variations in the pressure of the clay in the mouthpiece set up variations of strain in the metal of the mouthpiece which are measured by the strain gauge and indicated by a pointer and scale fitted in a convenient position. The water control valve was operated by hand using the pointer and scale to indicate whether more or less water was required.

Actually what is required is to control the consistency of the clay and this can be done by controlling the pressure in the mouthpiece. A device developed by the British Ceramic Research Association, Fig. 113, uses a steel pressure pad inserted in the mouthpiece and supported by a flexible rubber diaphragm. On the outside of the mouthpiece is a flexible metallic bellows, oil filled and fitted with a pressure gauge. A similar device developed by Messrs. Karl Händle & Söhne of Mühlacker, Germany, Fig. 114, uses a hemispherical rubber bulb instead of the bellows. Both these devices can be made to control the consistency of the clay automatically by including a hydraulically controlled water valve operated by the oil pressure in the bellows or bulb. A stop valve in the water supply pipe is coupled to the clutch lever on the machine and a solenoid-controlled valve is connected in the

Fig. 113   Moisture Controller. B.Ceram.R.A. Design. Detail of bellows, pressure gauge and water control valve

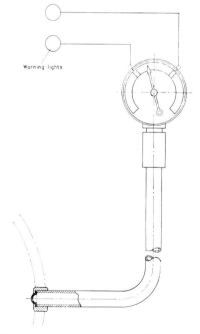

Fig. 114   Moisture Controller—Händle Design

driving motor circuit, so that the water supply is automatically cut off if the extruder is stopped either by disengaging the clutch or if the electric motor is stopped deliberately or accidentally. Little imagination is required to convert the hydraulic control into an electronic control based on the same principle. The pressure-measuring element would be changed from a hydraulic bellows to a pressure transducer containing strain gauges, forming an electrical bridge. In the hydraulic system the bellows pressure element is coupled directly to the hydraulically operated water-control valve, but in the electronic system the control is more complicated. A source of low voltage direct current is applied across the bridge which is balanced when clay of the desired consistency is being extruded. If the consistency of the clay changes, the balance of the bridge is upset and current flows, which is detected by a controller-regulator which tries to restore the balance by regulating the supply of water by operating the control valve. Such devices can be constructed by most electronic control manufacturers using standard units. Although all these work on the same principle, controlled by the consistency of the clay, variations in circuit design prevent direct comparison. However, the principle of operation is the important thing and it is considered that the consistency is the only property of the clay that it is desirable to measure and control.

A system developed in the U.S.A. is that of the Foxboro Company which measures the consistency of the clay indirectly from the pressure of the die-lubricating fluid which is supplied to the die under pressure by a positive displacement pump. If the consistency of the clay gets stiffer the pressure of the lubricating fluid increases and if the clay gets softer the lubricating pressure falls. In this case the water addition is controlled by the variations in lubrication pressure. The system is shown diagrammatically by Fig. 115, which shows the die oil lubrication supply line coupled to a consistency recording controller; this sends out a primary pneumatic signal which sets the control point of a flow controller in the water line to the mixer. The flow controller positions a proportional water-control valve in the water line to maintain a controlled rate of flow irrespective of pressure variations or surges in the water line. A second output from the duplex consistency controller operates a safety valve to add water only in cases of

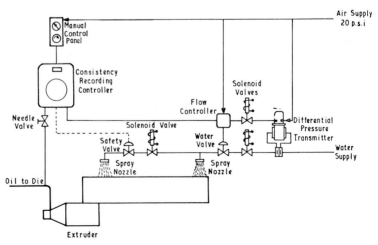

Fig. 115   Moisture Controller—Foxboro

extreme upsets, actuated at a predetermined high back-pressure value, and is normally inactive. The three solenoid-operated valves are electrically in parallel with the clay-feeder motor and stop the flow of water immediately the feeder is stopped. The above system can only be operated if the die is lubricated by oil or water delivered by a positive displacement pump. It will not operate if the die is lubricated by steam or if it has no lubrication. In such cases a similar system is used except that the primary consistency measurement is obtained from the loading of the electric motor driving the extruder.

In all the methods of control mentioned it is essential that the rate of feed of clay to the extruder should be maintained constant because variations in the rate of feed have the same effect on pressure or power consumption as variations in moisture content. If the feed rate falls, the pressure and power consumption also fall and the control interprets this as an increase in the water content of the clay being extruded and so reduces the water supply. Where control of the feed rate has been adopted, the simple hydraulic control has successfully controlled the moisture content within closer limits than $\pm \frac{1}{2}$ per cent which is considerably closer than is possible by manual tempering which depends upon the whims and fancies of an operator who judges the consistency by its appearance or feel. The electronic controls mentioned should be capable of at least a similar degree of control.

For many materials the measurement of the electrical conductivity of the material gives a measure of the moisture content, but for soils and clays this method has proved unsuccessful because the reading is extremely sensitive to packing density and contact effects; also, since water conducts electricity mainly by virtue of the electrolytes (soluble salts) it contains, the conductivity will be affected by a change in concentration of soluble salts even when the water content is constant.

The measurement of capacity would appear to be fundamentally more reliable. The method is based on the increase in capacity produced when the air dielectric between the plates of a condenser is replaced by a sample of the material. Since the dielectric constant of water is about 80 times that of air, and about 15 to 20 times that of dry clay, the measurement is obviously mainly dependent on the water present. It therefore measures total water and so is sensitive to packing density. Tests show that temperature affects the reading; heating a test specimen through 35 degrees F. caused the instrument to indicate an increase in moisture despite any drying which might have taken place because of the heating. It is also difficult to obtain reproducible results unless the surface of the specimen is perfectly flat. If considerable care is taken to ensure that the moisture distribution is uniform throughout the sample it is possible to measure the average moisture content correct to about ± 3 per cent. If however there is a moisture gradient throughout the specimen then the accuracy is more likely to be ± 8 per cent.

A method suggested by the Atomic Energy Research Establishment is that known as 'neutron moderation'. This requires a source of high-energy (epithermal) neutrons which bombard the specimen being tested. When the high-energy neutrons collide with the hydrogen atoms in the moisture in the clay body, the hydrogen atoms absorb some of their energy so that they become low-energy (thermal) neutrons which can be detected and measured even in the presence of high-energy neutrons. The reading would therefore be proportional to the number of hydrogen atoms in the neutron beam. Elements other than hydrogen have negligible effect on the reading, but allowance must be made for any hydrogen atoms that may be present other than in free water. To measure percentage moisture content by this method it is essential that the specimen must always be of constant thickness and uniform packing density. Monitoring the moisture content of an extruded column would appear to be possible by this method although the equipment would be very expensive.

A method suggested by Ekco Electronics is to bombard the specimen with gamma rays emitted by a radio-active isotope. Some of the rays will be absorbed by the specimen and by measuring the rays which pass through, by means of a scintillation counter, an indication of the moisture content of the specimen is obtained. Again it is essential that the specimens are of constant thickness and uniform packing density, which suggests that the extruded column is the most suitable place to make the measurement and this position is also the most suitable to mask the gamma rays to protect operatives. This system also is expensive and the source of gamma rays would need to be renewed from time to time.

Another method which has been suggested is to measure the attenuation of electro-magnetic waves passing through the extruded column. This is the Microwave Moisture Meter and consists of two separate transistorized units, one of which transmits, through a horn, radio waves at a frequency of 3,000 Mc/s. ± 30 Mc/s. and having a mean power of $\frac{1}{2}$ watt. The receiver has a similar horn, which collects the waves, coupled by a short waveguide to an attenuator and crystal detector, followed by a high-gain selective amplifier, a second detector and an indicating meter. The transmitter and receiver are set up with their horns facing each other at the same distance apart as they will be when testing a sample. The attenuator reading corresponding to centre scale indication on the meter is noted. The specimen to be tested is placed between the horns and the attenuator reading which gives centre scale indication is again noted. The difference between this and the initial reading is a measure of the attenuation due to the moisture content of the sample.

This instrument has been used satisfactorily for the measurement of the moisture content of solid walls but has not been used, up to the time of writing, for the measurement of the moisture content of extruded clay columns.

Some brickworks may be fortunate enough to have a clay supply whose moisture content does not fluctuate, seasonal variations being more of a gradual drift. In such cases the final moisture may be controlled very simply by feeding the clay into the mixer with an automatic weigh feeder which regulates the supply of tempering water automatically according to the weight of clay fed to the mixer. For such a control to be satisfactory the supply water should be at constant pressure, and the moisture content of the incoming clay should be checked at regular intervals so that adjustments may be made to the water control to allow for any drift.

A method of water control developed by a Swiss firm consists of a measuring head (Fig. 116) fitted with two spring-loaded arms, one of which carries a flat-faced roller and the other a narrow round-edged roller. The two rollers run on the top face of the extruded column, the broad-face roller scans the surface of the column whilst the other, suspended and oscillating, penetrates the column to an extent which depends upon the stiffness of

108

the clay. The depth of penetration is converted to an electrical quantity, which is proportional to the stiffness, and this electrical signal can be amplified to operate a control valve and recorder. Visible and audible warning signals can be fitted if desired.

The problem of automatically controlling the moisture content of clays is receiving serious consideration in many countries, particularly for clays which are to be formed by extrusion, and whilst considerable progress has been made there is still room for developments.

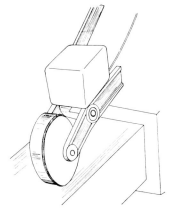

Fig. 116   Moisture Controller—Bühler Bros.

A recent development due to M.E.C. Stedham[2] uses the variation in the conductivity of clays at varying moisture contents as a means of controlling the amount of tempering water added to the clay mix in a double-shaft mixer. The bulk of the water is added at a constant rate and the remainder, approximately 3 per cent, is added through a spray nozzle at a varying rate controlled by the conductivity measurement. We have already mentioned that the relationship between conductivity and moisture content is by no means stable, since it is affected by the amount of soluble salts in the particular clay mix. Consequently the control was not satisfactory until an over-riding control in the form of a pressure or consistency controller, similar to that developed by the B.Ceram.R.A., was incorporated; not to control the water valve, but to vary, according to the consistency of the extruded column, the setting of the moisture controller. The system can also accept a stiffness or consistency signal provided by the current in the driving motor. It has been developed in conjunction with Negretti and Zambra Ltd., from standard pneumatic control instruments, and is generally as shown diagrammatically by Fig. 117.

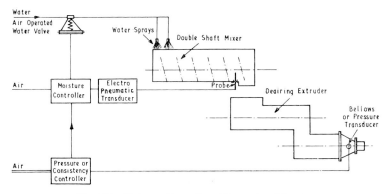

Fig. 117   Moisture Controller—Negretti and Zambra

Ref. 2. Trans. Brit. Ceram. Soc. Vol. 61, 1962.

As a quality control check the making moisture content should be measured at regular intervals, but this should be done by weighing a sample of the clay fed to the shaping machine, and then drying and reweighing the sample.

Quality Control: Brickmaking is repetition work and all bricks made to the same specification should have, as nearly as possible, the same dimensions, weight, colour, porosity and crushing strength, but no matter how strict the control over all the manufacturing processes complete sameness is impossible of achievement. Recorded measurements are never identical and the differences are not due merely to errors of measurement but do actually exist in the articles themselves.

If an average value is quoted it must be recognized that there must inevitably be variations above and below the average that cannot be eliminated in any circumstances. It is for this reason that manufacturing tolerances are allowed.

It is impossible to forecast the exact value of any particular characteristic of any one of a number of similar articles. We cannot foretell the exact length, or weight, of a particular brick, nor can we estimate its crushing strength exactly, but if the conditions of manufacture are generally stable then it is possible to define with a high degree of accuracy the limits within which, in the long run, any desired percentage of the values will fall. To do this necessitates the use of statistical analysis although, fortunately, it is unnecessary to understand the mathematical theory to be able to make practical use of it.

When introducing Quality Control to a manufacturing process do not attempt anything ambitious for a start. Preferably choose a simple dimension, that is easy to measure, such as the length or weight of a green brick. After experience has been gained with one simple dimension the system may be extended gradually until every operation in the manufacturing process is brought under control.

The total production from any one machine is divided into a number of sub-groups, usually by time intervals. Suppose, for example, that a subgroup represents half a day's make. Take a sample consisting of two or more, up to a maximum of ten, consecutive bricks as they come from the machine about half way through the morning and afternoon shifts.

Measure the desired dimension carefully on each individual in the sample. Add these measurements together and divide the sum by the number of bricks in the sample. This gives the sample mean, or average, usually denoted by '$\bar{x}$'. Subtract the smallest from the largest measurement in the sample. This gives the sample range, usually denoted by 'w'.

Plot the mean of each sample and the range of each sample on graphs on the same piece of graph paper. It is advisable to have a common form of chart for all Quality Control charts, and it is desirable to use squared paper divided into $\frac{1}{10}$ inch squares; 1 mm squares have been found to be inconveniently small.

When ten samples have been taken, and their means and ranges plotted on the charts, add all ten sample means together and divide the sum by ten so obtaining the Grand Mean, or average of averages, usually denoted by '$\bar{X}$'. Add all sample ranges together and divide the sum by ten to get the average range denoted by '$\bar{w}$'.

The control limits are now fixed in the following way.

Two numbers, denoted by A and D, which depend upon the number of components in each sample are taken from the following table.

110

No. in Sample	2	3	4	5	6	7	8	9	10
A	1·94	1·05	0·75	0·59	0·50	0·43	0·38	0·35	0·32
D	4·12	2·98	2·57	2·34	2·21	2·11	2·04	1·99	1·93

Calculate $A\bar{w}$ and $D\bar{w}$.

On the chart of averages draw Control Lines, in pencil, at $\bar{X}+A\bar{w}$ and $\bar{X}-A\bar{w}$.

On the chart of sample ranges draw lines, in pencil, at $\bar{w}$ and $D\bar{w}$. The line $D\bar{w}$ is the control limit.

When a further fifteen samples have been taken and their averages and ranges plotted, the values of $\bar{X}$, $\bar{w}$, $\bar{X}+A\bar{w}$, $\bar{X}-A\bar{w}$, and $D\bar{w}$, from the whole of the 25 samples now available should be calculated. The lines $\bar{X}$ and $\bar{w}$ may now be drawn on the charts in black ink and the other three, the control limits, in red ink to distinguish them clearly on the charts.

Once the Control Limits have been established no point, either average or range, should be allowed to fall outside them without investigation of the reason for its having done so, and without some action being taken to prevent, if possible, a recurrence of the production fault which caused it to fall outside the limit. In doing this repeatedly every time a wild point appears, and looking into the reason for consecutive points approaching the limit, it is hoped that faults will be detected and corrected one by one, until finally a state is reached in which the points rarely fall outside their Control Limits. The process is then said to be 'under control'.

Wear of dies, or mould liners, will cause a drift of average dimensions and weights towards the upper control limits, but if everything else is constant the range will not be affected. Variations in the constitution of the clay, in water content and distribution, in grading analysis, and wear in machines such as muller tyres, grinding plates, and grids, in the pan, wear of rolls, mixer blades and, in the case of extrusion machines, wear of pug knives, augers, and wing knives usually result in increasing the range.

Quality control charts therefore enable one to keep a check on the maintenance of machines as well as on the preparation of the clay and the actual forming process.

15 : Good Housekeeping

With the general clamouring for labour from all industries, it is only natural that workers will drift to those industries which are most amenable. The average worker will not have heavy manual work and dirty or dusty conditions if he can avoid them.

Many brickworks are however notorious places for dust. How can it be eliminated?

The only way is to take steps to reduce the amount of dust produced and to remove it as quickly as possible with the minimum of disturbance.

In the dry process the most prolific producers of dust are the dry pans and screens, because it is in the dry pan that the fines are produced whilst at the screens there is the greatest disturbance of fine particles. In other industries it is quite common practice to totally enclose dry pans and the sooner brickmakers realize the amount of damage and wear caused by dust the sooner will they take steps to reduce it by totally enclosing all dry pans and other machines which produce dust.

The pan and runners should be enclosed in a hood which is coupled to a dust extraction fan and filter, and the feed openings should be as small as possible, which implies mechanical feeders. The air velocity through the feed openings should be 100 to 150 ft. per minute. Such an air velocity will prevent dust escaping into the shop but is not sufficient to carry away fines from the pan itself because the air velocity inside the hood is extremely low.

Bucket elevators are usually totally enclosed, but it should be remembered that the source of dust is the point at which maximum disturbance of the ground material takes place, i.e. in the boot where the material is picked up, and again at the discharge. These parts should therefore be fitted with hoods coupled to the exhaust system. Again the air velocity should be 100 to 150 feet per minute through the openings.

Screens should also be covered and exhausted. If the screens are totally enclosed, light, tight fitting doors should be provided for inspection and changing of screens, and the hood should be coupled to the exhaust system to provide an air flow through the working openings of 100 to 150 feet per minute. If the screens are not totally enclosed but are fitted only with an overhead hood the volume of air should be about 75 to 100 cubic feet per minute for each square foot of screen area.

Another source of dust is in the cleaning of the shops. When floors are swept with a brush much dust is raised which floats about in the atmosphere for a considerable period. This consists of the finest dust, and it is just these very fine particles which are most likely to find their way into machine mechanisms and into the lungs of operatives and are therefore the most dangerous. For this reason the cleaning of shops by means of vacuum cleaning brushes attached to the end of flexible hose coupled to a ring main, having coupling points at suitable intervals, which is connected to a central vacuum cleaning plant is recommended. By this means the dust is collected with the minimum of disturbance and there is no dispersion of dust to settle on machines, walls and stillages. To do this efficiently necessitates a compact layout but it is well worth while and is in use at some Continental works and is very popular in the pottery industry in this country.

Another feature of 'Good Housekeeping' is the working conditions in the factory. Lighting without glare and without shadows; heating and ventilation to give comfortable working conditions; the painting of walls and ceilings in light pastel shades in order to create the impression of spaciousness and to reflect light from their surfaces in order to economize in artificial light; having a place for everything and everything in its place; such conditions are not pampering to the workers but are economically sound.

Clean conditions together with adequate lighting, heating and ventilation are the first steps in 'Good Housekeeping' which should be insisted upon by all managements. 'Good Housekeeping' appeals to the visual and psychological needs of the worker, it assists in the recruitment and retention in the industry of a better class of worker and gives to them a feeling of security and cleanliness. Orderliness and efficiency of the works breeds these same characteristics in the workers themselves. Nothing gives the impression of orderliness and efficiency so much as a clear, unobstructed floor, transit area or passage, with the work moving smoothly from operation to operation without pause. The shop floor is not a store room and every time an article is put down it earns nothing, does not increase in value, and costs money to put down and pick up again. It is therefore a form of waste.

16 : Mechanization

Unnecessary handling and transport is another form of waste, particularly manual handling and transport, and it is for this reason that there are so many mechanical handling devices on the market today. Human effort is the most expensive form of power it is possible to buy. A good manual worker is capable of averaging between 3,000 and 4,000 ft. lb. of work per minute over an 8-hour day. 1 h.p. is equivalent to 33,000 ft. lb. of work per minute, so that a 1 h.p. electric motor is capable of doing as much work as 10 good labourers. Of course to perform the work the motor has to operate through a machine, but if the mechanical efficiency of the machine is only 20 per cent, a 5 h.p. motor and machine together will do as much work as 10 men, or will do the work of 1 man 10 times as quickly, and the running cost will be only in the region of pence per hour. In general, therefore, it pays to install mechanical aids wherever possible, even though it may mean reorganizing the work, provided the operation is standardized for a sufficiently long time for the savings entailed to be sufficient to pay for the cost, installation and maintenance, of the machine and to show a reasonable profit. It is in the field of unskilled and semi-skilled labour that machines can be expected to provide maximum savings in production costs so releasing men for upgrading into more productive and more lucrative jobs. To employ men for their muscular strength alone is a misuse of human labour. Men have the power of thinking and of making decisions which enables them to control the machines they operate and it is for this power that men should be employed. Since the greatest part of the unskilled worker's job is concerned with handling and transport it is in this field that maximum economies can be effected and that maximum number of mechanical aids are available.

The types of mechanical handling devices to adopt depend very largely upon the layout of the works and it is impossible to lay down any hard and fast rules. So many different types of mechanical shovels, hoists, cranes, elevators, conveyors, feeders, mechanical trucks, etc. have been designed solely for the purpose of doing just those jobs which are so irksome to the average workman that there should be no great difficulty in choosing the most suitable for any particular works. Since all works are different in layout some of the devices need to be specially made to suit the particular environment and sometimes re-arrangement of the plant may be desirable. For mechanical trucks and fork-lift trucks good roadways are essential.

On all brickworks a considerable amount of capital is invested in plant, buildings, roads and equipment and the function of maintenance is to safeguard that investment.

During the past 20 years ideas on maintenance have changed. It is no longer looked upon as a department for repairing broken down machines, its main function is to prevent machines from breaking down. It can be looked upon as an insurance against loss of production and so like any other insurance policy must always be operative.

Maintenance is necessitated by wear and so everything possible should be done to reduce wear to the absolute minimum.

Different parts of a machine are subject to different types of wear and so need different treatment. All machines consist of two essential parts, the mechanism and the working point. The mechanism consists of the drive, transmission, gears, bearings, etc. which serve to transmit the power from the driving unit to the working point. The working point of the machine is that part which actually performs the work on the material to be processed. Wear of the mechanism is generally due to the frictional abrasion of metal against metal and to reduce this the surfaces in contact should be smooth and well lubricated.

Lubrication: There are two types of lubrication, one is known as 'boundary' lubrication and the other as 'fluid film' lubrication. Boundary lubrication is that type in which the oil is adsorbed in the pores of the metal, and is the usual type of lubrication found in slow-moving machines such as brick-making machines. Fluid film lubrication is effected when two surfaces, suitably designed to form a convergent oil wedge, run together at high speed in the presence of an ample supply of lubricant or when fed by lubricant under pressure from a pump.

Boundary Lubrication: A good surface finish may appear to be perfectly smooth both to the sight and touch but by suitable magnification it can be shown that the surface is by no means perfectly smooth but consists of a number of needle-like projections. If two pieces of metal are brought together they will touch at only a few of the tips of those projections so that the actual area of contact is extremely small and even under light loads the local intensity of pressure is extremely high. In the absence of lubrication these points of contact will become welded together under the pressure and there can be no relative movement until these welds have been sheared. In shearing the fracture occurs in the weaker material and some of the weaker material is carried away attached to the projections of the stronger material. Since there has been removal of metal, wear has taken place. To prevent this it is necessary to interpose between the two surfaces some material which is not easily penetrated, so keeping the points apart, and of low shearing strength to offer little resistance to the movement of the two surfaces. This material is the lubricant, generally oil. Oil is fluid and, when applied to the surfaces, fills the depressions which act as a very large number of tiny oil reservoirs from which the oil is drawn by capillary action when the two surfaces are in relative movement. These oil reservoirs are extremely small and soon empty so that frequent replenishment is necessary. They should never be allowed to run dry or metal to metal contact will occur with consequent excessive wear. It is therefore imperative that a regular lubrication drill be instituted if maximum life is required from machines.

Straight mineral oils are preferred for all machines unless special circumstances necessitate special additives. Generally speaking the heavier the load, the slower the speed, and the greater the clearance, the higher should be the viscosity of the oil. Conversely, lighter loads, higher speeds and smaller clearances need a lower viscosity oil.

As soon as a new machine starts to run wear commences. The tiny needle-like projections are rubbed down and, if done in the presence of an ample supply of lubricant, the minute fragments of metal which break off are washed away by the lubricant doing no harm and the metal surfaces become highly polished. If however there is not sufficient lubricant to wash the metal particles away they remain between the two contacting surfaces and cause scratching of the surfaces and further wear. Therefore during the early life of any machine it pays to use an excessive amount of oil until such time as optimum surfaces are obtained, after which the amount of oil used may be reduced although the rubbing surfaces should never be allowed to run dry.

Dust is the main enemy of lubrication. Fine particles of dust entering with the oil, or through the clearance space between the two moving surfaces, mix with the oil to form a lapping paste which rapidly causes excessive wear. Even dust which is too fine to be seen by the naked eye will cause rapid wear. This emphasizes the necessity for absolute cleanliness both in the storage and application of lubricant. Dust in the atmosphere should be kept to a minimum by introducing the methods advised in the section on 'Good Housekeeping'.

The lubrication of machines should be done at regular intervals every day and in the case of those machines fitted with automatic lubrication the oil reservoirs should be kept topped up.

It is always advisable to enclose gears in a dust-proof enclosure and wherever possible to have them totally enclosed and running in an oil bath.

Even with such precautions wear is bound to take place. The main function of the maintenance department is to maintain machines in optimum condition and this can only be done by regular inspection of the mechanism, and immediate adjustment of the clearance between rubbing surfaces such as bearings, slides, etc., tightening of loose nuts, pins and keys, in fact counteracting the effects of wear as it becomes evident.

The working points of the machines are subject to the most abrasive wear because they work in direct contact with the clay. They consist of such things as the mullers, grinding plates, grids and scrapers in pan mills, the rollers of crushing rolls, the knives in mixers and pugs, the augers, shredder plates and dies in extruders, the dies on presses, in fact every part of any machine which is subject to direct abrasive wear by the clay. Every effort should be made to reduce the amount of this wear. The clay cannot be altered so attention must be turned to the use of some of the special abrasion-resisting metals which have been developed.

Abrasion-resisting Metals: In clay-working machinery the working points are usually of cast iron but this is a rather ambiguous statement today when so many different types of cast iron are available. In recent years a number of abrasion-resisting alloy cast irons have been developed, the main alloying constituent being chromium.

High-carbon, high-chromium alloy cast irons are particularly resistant to abrasion. Such an alloy cast iron having about 28 to 30 per cent of chromium and 2·6 to 2·8 per cent carbon has an abrasion resistance about 20 times as great as a good quality grey cast iron, and if heat-treated by soaking at 1,040 degrees C. for 1 hour and then allowed to cool in still air its abrasion resistance is considerably increased.

Such abrasion-resisting cast irons can only be machined after annealing. Annealing is effected by heating the metal to 800 degrees C. for 12 to 24 hours and allowing to cool in the furnace, or in still air. They easily work-harden and so if they cannot be finished to size by a single machining operation it may be necessary to anneal before each cut. Machining should be carried out with tools tipped with carbide or sintered alumina, and deep cuts should be taken to get under the hard skin. Castings in this material are now made by the 'Truprocess' of precision casting, by Messrs. Darwins of Sheffield, who can by this method produce accurate castings which can be finished to size by grinding.

It must be remembered, however, that alloy cast irons having such a high carbon content, although most abrasion resistant, tend to be brittle and so should not be used for parts subject to severe impact. Decrease in the alloying constituents, carbon and chromium, reduces the abrasion resistance but increases the ductility. In a similar way the addition of nickel increases the ductility and toughness but reduces the abrasion resistance. Varying the amount of the alloying constituents makes a very wide range of abrasion-resisting alloy cast irons available, suitable for the majority of clay-working machines, and it is always advisable to consult the manufacturers in order that the correct grade may be obtained for any particular duty.

In the case of steels, chromium is again the most important alloying constituent for abrasion resistance but steels have lower carbon contents than cast irons and so to get the best out of alloy steels they should be correctly hardened and tempered. Again the manufacturers should be consulted to obtain the most suitable steel and the optimum hardening conditions for the particular duty for which the part is to be used.

Another method of increasing the life of such wearing parts as ploughs and scrapers in grinding pans, the lips of excavator buckets or digging teeth, mixer blades, pug knives and augers, the projections on kibbling rolls and many other parts which are subject to local wear is to use a hard-surfacing welding rod. This practice of reclaiming worn parts is practised to a great extent in this country but far greater use is made of the process in the U.S.A. where even muller tyres are built up with abrasion-resisting hard-surfacing welding rod.

Planned Maintenance: All machine parts do not need attention at the same time or with the same frequency. Their life depends upon the conditions under which they work. Because of this, at far too many works, no-one knows the frequency at which parts have to be adjusted or replaced. There is no planning, and maintenance is carried out as and when necessary.

The introduction of a planned maintenance system involves the introduction of a record card for every machine, the first entry, in the case of a new machine, being the date of installation. Thereafter every adjustment, replacement or repair, however trivial, should be entered on the card together with the date on which the job is done. With a record card for every machine it will soon be possible to obtain from them an estimate of the frequency with which the machine requires attention. It is then possible to

116

draw up a rota of inspection for every machine, and to plan this rota beforehand, so that a schedule of work for the maintenance department can be drawn up well in advance of the date on which the work is to be done. Much of the work will necessarily be in the nature of preventive maintenance, by which is meant taking measures to counteract the effects of wear in order to prevent the necessity for more serious maintenance later. Such a scheme is known as 'planned maintenance'. It consists of a regular, systematic and intelligent inspection of all machines, immediate attention to minor running adjustments, the keeping of accurate records and the planning of the maintenance work. The adjustment of loose slides or bearings, the tightening of loose nuts or keys and suchlike minor adjustments may be done by the inspector at the time of the inspection but should be noted on the record card for that particular machine. The inspection should however be thorough and notes should be made of any complaints about the operation of the machine by the usual operator and checks made to see if they are justified. From such an inspection a full and detailed report should be made of all the work which the maintenance department has to carry out. An estimate of the time required to carry out the work is made, the cost and availability of spares and material are checked and arrangements are made with the production department to release the machine for maintenance on the date scheduled.

The record charts provide a life history of the wear of each part of every machine from which it is possible to estimate very closely, indeed almost exactly, when adjustments or maintenance will be necessary. A programme of maintenance work can then be drawn up, covering a period of twelve months, the actual dates of inspection and the date on which maintenance work will commence being definitely stated. The frequency of individual items of maintenance can be noted and steps taken to reduce their incidence by the use of abrasion-resisting metals, by hard facing or even by a modification to the design. This is one of the main advantages of planned maintenance; to ensure that maximum benefit is obtained from past experience and to eliminate known weaknesses. Another is that the production department knows beforehand exactly which machines will be out of production for maintenance on any particular day and can plan their production programme accordingly. This ensures that the plant operates at maximum productivity for the longest possible period of time and, although records have to be kept, overall production costs are reduced because all staff, both production and maintenance, are fully utilized.

Acknowledgements

British Ceramic Research Association—for Figs. 1, 2, 26, 35, 51, 59, 60, 65, 83, 84, 112, 113.

J. Schmidheiny & Co. A.G.—for Figs. 3, 4.

Rieterwerke—for Figs. 5, 53.

Bradley and Craven Ltd.—for Figs. 12, 27, 42, 88, 89, 90, 91, 92, 107, 108.

Edgar Allen and Co. Ltd.—for Figs. 13, 17, 20.

C. Whittaker and Co. Ltd.—for Figs. 14, 100, 102, 111.

Tyne Metal Co. Ltd.—for Fig. 15.

British Jeffrey-Diamond Ltd.—for Figs. 16, 43.

Electromagnets Ltd.—for Fig. 18.

Laeis-Werke A.G.—for Figs. 19, 76.

Keramik-Maschinen G.m.b.H.—for Fig. 21.

Karl Händle & Söhne—for Figs. 22, 44, 56, 114.

Clayton, Goodfellow and Co. Ltd.—for Figs. 23, 55, 101.

James Mitchell and Son—for Fig. 24.

Thos. C. Fawcett Ltd.—for Figs. 25, 109.

J. C. Steele and Sons—for Figs. 29, 80.

Alfred Herbert Ltd.—for Fig. 30.

Alpine A.G.—for Fig. 31.

Henry Simon Ltd.—for Fig. 32.

N. Greening and Sons Ltd.—for Figs. 33, 34.

Pegson Ltd.—for Fig. 36.

International Combustion Products Ltd.—for Figs. 37, 41.

West's Gas Improvement Co. Ltd.—for Fig. 39.

Lockers (Engineers) Ltd.—for Figs. 40, 61, 62.

Steele and Cowlishaw Ltd.—for Fig. 45.

Foster, Yates and Thom Ltd.—for Fig. 46.

Liner Concrete Machinery Co. Ltd.—for Figs. 47, 48.

Apex Construction Ltd.—for Fig. 49.

Soest-Ferrum Apparatebau G.m.b.H.—for Figs. 52, 67, 68, 74.

John Whitehead and Co. Ltd.—for Fig. 54.

Conveyors (Ready Built) Ltd.—for Fig. 57.

Rawdon Ltd.—for Fig. 58.

Berry and Son—for Fig. 63.

Posey Iron Works Inc.—for Fig. 64.

C. Keller & Co.—for Figs. 66, 94.

Weserhütte Otto Wolff G.m.b.H.—for Fig. 69.

International Clay Machinery Co.—for Fig. 70.

Fate-Root-Heath Co.—for Figs. 71, 72, 73.

Gebr. Netzsch—for Fig. 75.

Service (Engineers) Ltd.—for Fig. 77.

Modern Industrial Appliances Ltd.—for Figs. 78, 79.

British Ceramic Society—for Figs. 81, 82.

Bennett and Sayer Ltd.—for Figs. 85, 86, 98, 99.

Wm. Johnson and Sons (Leeds) Ltd.—for Figs. 87, 105, 110.

Georg Willy A.G.—for Fig. 93.

Bason & Sons Ltd.—for Fig. 95.

Bentley & Garforth—for Fig. 96.

Jesshope Engineering Division of Wm. Boulton Ltd.—for Fig. 97.

Spengler-Maschinenbau G.m.b.H.—for Fig. 103.

Chisholm, Boyd & White Co.—for Fig. 104.

Buhler Bros.—for Fig. 116.

Foxboro-Yoxall Ltd.—for Fig. 115.

M.E.C. Stedham in conjunction with Negretti and Zambra Ltd.—for Fig. 117.

Index

124